# THE ASIAN FACE

*Touches of beauty should never be halfway.*

—Keats

# THE ASIAN FACE

## A Styling Guide

Gloria Noda

*Foreword by*
**Bill Blass**

KODANSHA INTERNATIONAL LTD.
Tokyo, New York and San Francisco

For Mira, Carrie, and Kay.

**Editor's Acknowledgments**
The editor wishes to thank the following people for their encouragement and assistance in the early stages of making this book: S. Funatake, Linda Furuyama, Sandie Ishikawa, Mamie Kamada, Ann Kambara, Michiyo Kashiwagi, Mary Lee, Jo Morohashi, Dawn Narita, Sheri Shimada, Merilee Tanbara, Mari Taketa, Florence Tanabe, and Emi Yamauchi. Special thanks to Keiko Adachi, Allan Akita, George Akita, Jin Iwai, Suzanna Kawamura, Christine Menton, Bette Nomura, Masako Oyama, Chris Pearce, Nina Raj, Rowena Wildin, Eiko Yamada, Glenn Yoshimori, and Erika Young. Mahalo to all—LSO.

**Credits**
Photo of Bill Blass, courtesy Bill Blass, Ltd.; photos of Nora Akino and Jae Eun Choi by Kaku Kurita; photo of Ramona Auyong by Stephen Riede; photo of Alene de la Houssaye by Beth Baptiste; photo of Mariko Yandell by H. Mack Horton; photos of hair styles on p. 96, courtesy of Fumio Kawashima. Illustrations by Eiko Ikeda. Graphics and layout by Hideyo Senoh.

**Note to the Reader**
Readers with sensitive skin or hair are advised to consult with a specialist before trying any of the products, techniques, or recipes mentioned in this book. Always check the ingredients and read the instructions carefully before using any product.

Distributed in the United States by Kodansha International/USA Ltd., through Harper & Row, Publishers, Inc., 10 East 53rd Street, New York, New York 10022. Published in Japan and the United States by Kodansha International Ltd., 12–21, Otowa 2-chome, Bunkyo-ku, Tokyo 112 and Kodansha International/USA Ltd., with offices at 10 East 53rd Street, New York, New York 10022 and the Hearst Building, 5 Third Street, Suite No. 400, San Francisco, California 94103. Copyright © 1986 by Kodansha International Ltd. All rights reserved. Printed in Japan.

First edition, 1986

**Library of Congress Cataloging in Publication Data**
Noda, Gloria.
  The Asian Face.

  1.  Beauty, Personal.     2.  Women, Oriental.
3.  Skin—Care and hygiene.     4.  Cosmetics.
5.  Hairdressing.     I.  Title.
RA778.N776     1985       646.7'042        85-40057
ISBN 0-87011-731-9
ISBN 4-7700-1231-4 (in Japan)

# CONTENTS

# FOREWORD

Gloria Noda is that sophisticate of the world—ever-observing, understanding, and completely knowledgeable of the places she works in and visits. Her frequent global explorations—to Europe, America, and Asia—give her a unique overview and understanding of beauty worldwide. From this comes particular understanding of Western ideas, as well as Asian, in matters of beauty and makeup.

What a great idea to have her viewpoint and opinions on makeup for women with Asian faces. Gloria understands that the basic ingredients of attractiveness have to do with health, skin care, tasteful makeup, clean hair, and diet—a total commitment to oneself.

In presenting my yearly fashion shows in Tokyo, Gloria is an invaluable consultant vis-à-vis makeup and the overall look of the mannequins, be they Western or Asian.

Few women truly understand Asian beauty as well as Gloria Noda. This book is a highly important guide from a true expert.

BILL BLASS

# 1 WHY STYLE YOUR FACE?

Your skin, your eyes, your nose and facial bone structure, and your hair are Asian. This is you. What you are behind this important exterior is totally up to you. The face that you present to the world, the first impression that people have of you, depends upon your looks.

What you make of these Asian features—whether you think of them as plus factors—whether you *use* them as plus factors in establishing your own personality—makes all the difference in how others see you.

Making up, emphasizing one feature, coloring another, gives you a chance to experiment with yourself, to define your personality in terms that other people respond to positively. It's fun, and you will see yourself differently.

When you see a different you, you act like a different person. Buying a new kind of jacket, or wearing a new skirt length that feels different against your legs, gives you a new movement, gives you a lift. It's the same with changing what you do to your face.

Makeup adds color, heightens your good points, and when you see yourself in the mirror, you feel a new confidence.

Confidence is a quality that other people respond to. It's a very basic reaction. Animals, for instance, respond immediately to confidence in people. It makes them feel secure. Confidence is attractive to everyone, people and animals alike.

There is a strong desire to be natural. But natural doesn't mean bare. In facestyling, natural means not wearing a mask. Facestyling is bringing out your good points, deemphasizing those weaker features that take away from your good ones. What you accomplish with facestyling is a more vibrant version of what you really are.

Looking good brings self-confidence, and a feeling of liking yourself that is most important. You are the one who knows yourself best, and the people around you accept your evaluation of yourself.

So, make the most of your Asian features. Know them well, and know what to do with your cheekbones, the planes of your face, and your eyes. Heighten your assets, make them especially interesting!

You have a number of strong plus factors that other faces—those of Caucasians, Blacks—don't have. You may not have thought about this. You're used to your face, and probably at some time in your life you have despaired over one or another part of it that you wished were different. This puts you right in line with the rest of the population. Everyone has agonized over not having different hair—or a different nose, or eyes, or ears, or figure.

Let's get on to those plus factors, the good points, that you should work with!

# 2 PLUS FACTORS

There are two sides to every coin. Because you may have considered your eyes, your skin texture, your high cheekbones, or your hair a minus point, let me remind you of what a strong plus factor each of these can be.

Let's talk about being noticed. Many women scheme, plot, and maneuver to be noticed. If you're not in a completely Asian environment, you stand out—you're noticed. This may not please you all the time, but you get what others find hard to achieve, and you get it without having to work for it.

*How* you're noticed is of course the important point. Whether you want to be noticed as a great gal—or an intelligent, efficient woman—or an important partner to a successful husband—or a truly glamourous woman—whatever your image, it's easier for you because you've achieved the first step, which is being noticed.

You probably have high cheekbones. Makeup books for women with Caucasian features spend a great deal of space and time explaining how to get a high-cheekbone look. Yours already are.

Eyes have been called "the window of the soul." They are the way you establish contact, and express your feelings. Most makeup techniques today center on the eyes—the most important part of the face. People notice your eyes immediately, because they look

different. This difference is a great plus factor, and one to be made the most of.

Your eyes allow more space for shadowing above the eye, because the space is not divided by a crease that conceals color, and because you do not have the protruding socket bone that Caucasian or Black eyes have to minimize. Layering and blending different shadows is much easier for you because you have the space to work the colors into.

Your skin tone and texture? They are very much a part of you, they complete your look. Because Asian skins have less hair than Caucasians or Blacks, the surface of the skin looks smoother, the pores tighter. Hollywood makeup men who work on Asian faces say that Asian skin fits differently over the bone structure. It is more smooth and firm, following the facial structure more closely, and there is a layer of oil under Asian skin that keeps it lubricated.

Anyone who reads about facial treatment creams knows that a smooth, poreless look is much admired. It is something to be taken care of carefully, because it's a strong plus factor for the future.

Your hair is another plus. Asian hair has a thicker shaft to each hair, and each hair is positioned further apart on the scalp. This results in shiny hair with a look of more volume, a definite plus. You probably don't have to battle limp hair, or pamper sensitive hair, but if you do need treatment, Asian hair responds well. Straight is great on you, when it is shaped with a good haircut. Or if you prefer the soft look of waves, permanent waves are easy to administer to Asian hair, according to our styling experts.

As you know by now, this is not a book of techniques to aid an Asian face in shedding its Asian qualities. That doesn't work, and it's not desirable. What is written and illustrated here is how to make the most of your plus factors, your features, what is you yourself.

# 3 DESIGNING YOUR LOOK
## *The Points to Consider*

What do you have to consider—how do you start your thinking—when deciding how you're going to look? We've consulted seven experts in the fields of dermatology, facestyling, and hairstyling. Here's who they are, and what they do.

Our dermatologists are Dr. Kiyoshi Toda, head of dermatology at Tokyo Teishin Hospital, and Dr. Carole Shear, dermatologist at the Cabrini Medical Center in New York. They talk of specific skin reactions, some of it applying only to Asian skin, and of care of the skin surface itself. The healthier your skin is, the easier it will be to work with, to project the look you find best for you.

Three makeup experts offer advice. Kimi Oshiro is the creative director at Shiseido, and is responsible for the face images at Paris fashion showings of designers Lanvin, Kenzo, Thierry Mugler, and Issey Miyake, as well as developing new Shiseido techniques. New York expert Arthur Scott designs glamourous looks for Chanel, *Harper's Bazaar*, and Italian *Vogue*, and does improvement techniques as well. Tyen of Christian Dior is the Vietnamese who originates the new cosmetic colors, the techniques of applying them, and the total Christian Dior makeup image each season in Paris. These three makeup artists share their ideas, and techniques, for achieving the look you want.

Their concern is that you have the right materials to work with, the most flattering or interesting colors to use, and that you know how to apply them in a way that shows your features to their best advantage.

These three experts speak of surfaces, of achieving highs and lows on the face.

One of the major characteristics of the Asian face is that it has a flat surface, like a plateau of land. To create surface interest, the bones and hollows should be designed to give surface variation. Catching the light here, providing shaping there, gives new life to a face. This is done through shadowing and highlighting different areas.

Analyzing your facial structure is an important part of determining what you are going to do in contouring the face. A three-way mirror, which allows you to see each profile as well as the front, is necessary for this. Or, use a hand mirror to catch the view of each side of your face while looking in a wall mirror.

Surprisingly, the distinction between single-fold, double-fold, and deep single-fold Asian eyes is considered by makeup technicians as a matter of facial individuality, and not of major importance in shadowing the eyes. However, they do have a slight change in technique for the double-fold eye.

Suga is the hairstylist who won international acclaim for his haircut for skating star Dorothy Hamill, and for actress/model Brooke Shields, as well as the beautiful head looks in *Vogue*. He says that the shape of the head, and the volume of hair in proportion to the body, is a major factor to consider in choosing a hairstyle. Suga advises using a full-length mirror to study your overall proportions when deciding on a hairstyle.

Fumio Kawashima is a trend-setting hairstylist in Tokyo, who worked in London doing creative styling for Vidal Sassoon, and does styling demonstrations throughout Asia. For Kawashima, the glossiness and texture of the hair are the prime factors to consider.

Each expert stresses that techniques do not have to be complicated, that there are simple procedures, and that it is more productive for you to know and master these basics than to involve yourself with a complicated beauty routine.

What follows is a consensus of the opinions of these experts who are deeply involved with face imagery. This information is presented for you here in detail, so that you can experiment and choose the best techniques and image for yourself.

Among those who have contributed to this book are eleven women with Asian features, who have shared their beauty regimens. Their biographies and their beauty routines reveal the individuality that makes these women outstanding.

Occasionally there will be a mention of specific brand names. These are simply suggestions and not necessarily the recommending of one brand over another. The people who share their expertise and beauty routines have their preferences, and have given examples of what they use in some cases. These have been included because they often are revealing as to the kind of product to be used. Apologies are extended to the other brands which might be equally as useful. The diversity that you will find should indicate the range of products that are available, and how easy it is to find the tools to use in devising your own special look.

# 4 ASIAN SKIN AND HAIR
## *The Fundamental Differences*

## ASIAN SKIN

Asian skin, having fewer hair pores, has a smoother surface. It also has a firmness in fitting over the facial bone structure that will be of benefit to you as you grow older. The normal loss of skin elasticity, which causes skin wrinkles and folds, is less noticeable for Asians than for other races. Also, the under-surface oil that Asian skins possess will act to your benefit in the aging process. Excessive dryness, a problem that age brings to other women, is much less apparent in Asian skin.

Asian skin contains more melanin granules. Melanin is what gives your skin its deeper pigmentation. It provides more protection against the sun's ultraviolet rays than skin with a lower melanin content can provide. But it also causes you to have sun reactions which absolutely require that you take sun protection measures.

### *The Effects of Melanin in Asian Skin*

Asian skin is more prone to what is known as hyper-pigmentation. That is, to darkening of parts of the skin surface. What in older people are seen as "liver spots," a darkening of small areas on the back of the hands, or on the face or arm, is more common with Asians.

Because of this, protection from the sun with sunscreening lotions is a necessity for your appearance, and the health of your skin, now and in the future. Sunscreens today contain PABA (para amino benzoic acid), a sunscreening agent which gives protection against ultraviolet rays. Most of the sunscreen preparations are numbered to indicate their sunscreening ability. Numbers will range from 2, the least protection, to as high as 20, which acts as a sun block. The numbering allows you to pace your skin's tanning reaction by starting off with a high protection factor until a tan has begun, and then to gradually allow more of the sun's rays to penetrate by switching to a lower screening number and effect.

Melanin also causes skin that has been scraped or cut to heal darker in color than the undisturbed area. Gradually, as the skin's surface cells sluff off, the healing area will return to normal skin tone and color. It is also possible that this melanin content will cause your skin to take more time to heal or, in some cases, to heal with an excess of scar tissue.

One of the positive effects of melanin is that it helps to protect the skin against skin cancer, and because of this, Asians are less liable to have skin cancer than lighter-skinned people.

## Skin Sensitivity

What your skin is sensitive to—its sensitivity level—depends more on food and water intake than it does on racial differences.

The Japanese are quite certain that their skin is more sensitive than other skins. To a certain extent, this is true. Dr. Kiyoshi Toda, head of dermatology at Tokyo Teishin Hospital, says that this is true concerning Japanese who live in Japan.

In a series of skin patch tests conducted at Harvard Medical School, it was determined that Japanese residing in Japan showed marked sensitivity of the skin, and were prone to allergic reactions. Sensitivity decreased with Japanese who spent three to six months in the United States. Sensitivity was markedly less than, or normal with U.S. levels, for Japanese residing in the United States and eating an American diet.

Dr. Toda noted that Japanese skin is not oily on the surface, due to the Japanese diet, which is low in the fats that generate lipids. Western food generates more lipids on the skin surface, providing a wax-like protective film, which reduces the surface skin's reaction to irritants.

An important point to note in skin sensitivity is what Asian skins are sensitive to. In experiments conducted by Clinique for their products being marketed in Japan, Clinique used separate groups of Japanese men and women living in New York, and tested them for skin sensitivity. Their information leads them to believe that the results apply to other Asians as well.

Test results revealed more sensitivity in Asians to alcohol, menthol, and salicylic acid. Many skin tonics, as well as after-shave preparations, contain alcohol and menthol. Menthol (or peppermint camphor) is also found in cigarettes and flavorings. Salicylic acid (or ortho-hydroxybenzoic acid) is found naturally in oil of wintergreen and commercially in aspirin and other pharmaceuticals, flavorings, and certain dyes. It is used as a skin-peeling agent in preparations designed to remove dead skin cells from the skin surface, in sunburn treatment creams, and in medication used to treat skin diseases.

It is worthwile—really worthwhile—to take a minute to read the contents of skin products that you buy. There are alternatives to all three of these agents that cause sensitivity. Witch hazel is a skin tonic that provides a pleasant cooling and firming sensation without disturbing sensitive skin. Face packs and scrubs—which are described in detail in a later chapter—remove dead surface cells without causing a skin reaction.

*Skin Metabolism*

Our two dermatologists agree that skin metabolism, the process that controls cell regeneration and body temperature control, is the same for Asians and non-Asians. The fact that the skin regeneration process is exactly the same would indicate that skin treatment products which feed cells, and stimulate their activity in creating oxygen and retaining moisture, work equally effectively on Asian skins as they do for other races.

## ASIAN HAIR

In contrast to other hair, the Asian hair shaft is thick, straight, and bends less. There are fewer hairs per square inch. The cuticle (outside coating) is smoother, and reflects more light, which gives an effect of more shine. The medulla (inside) contains more air pockets, which gives the hair shaft its thickness and straight quality. Although there are fewer hair shafts, the thickness of each shaft gives an effect of more volume, producing a look of luxurious hair.

The dark color of Asian hair is determined by the amount and type of melanin in it. Melanin, you will remember, also gives your skin its characteristic coloring.

Asian hair is easy to treat with permanent waving, according to Fumio Kawashima, one of our hairstylists who has worked extensively on both Asian and non-Asian hair. He explains, "It is easy to permanent Asian hair. It takes less time for the process. People think that because the hair shaft is thicker, it will take more time, but that isn't true. A weaker solution should be used. The pH point is lower."

Asian hair should be cut blunt. This is not a styling technique; it is a way of cutting the hair. A blunt cut has the ends cut straight across rather than a tapered cut, which "fringes" the hair. A blunt cut can be used for different lengths and hairstyles. International hairstylist Suga says, "The best cut for Asian hair is a blunt cut. It is the easiest to maintain, it looks better, and it shines more. With some Asian hair, the quality of the hair around the ears and the nape of the neck is different. That part of the cut might have to be tapered, but the general cut should be blunt."

Bear in mind that Asian heads are often flat at the back of the crown of the head. This area requires more volume. A good cut—slightly closer to the head than with non-Asian hair—is absolutely necessary.

# 5 CLEANSING, TONING, AND RE-SURFACING YOUR SKIN

## CLEANSING

Sixty percent of the women in the United States use soap to cleanse their face. If you do, check the wrapper and make sure that the soap is designed as a facial soap, or is a mild soap. Do not use a deodorant soap on your face, as the ingredients that curb odors are sometimes irritating to facial skin.

The natural pH (a measure of acidity or alkalinity) of your skin, is no different for Asians than for other races. However, to protect this normal pH balance of the skin, a mild soap is necessary. Dermatologists often suggest using *Dove* or *Basic*, examples of soaps that retain normal skin balance. Dr. Carole Shear of the Cabrini Medical Center says that *Ivory* is irritating to some adult skins.

If you wash your face, use warm water, and rinse thoroughly. If you use your hands, instead of a washcloth, to wash your face, rinse five times, with cool rinses for the last two times, since the splashing is not as effective as a washcloth in removing soap. Hot water, and cold water, are not good for the skin. The principle is the same as when you're washing woolens. The skin does not like extremes of temperature. Very hot or very cold water can cause the tiny underskin capillary veins to surface or break, giving a redness under the skin surface.

With cleansing cream, the routine is two applications of cream, creaming and tissuing off, creaming and tissuing off.

Eye makeup remover? Most women don't use it, but most should. For women with mature skins, whose skin has become thinner and more delicate, eye makeup remover is infinitely better than soap, or rubbing with a tissue after using a cleansing cream. For younger women *now* is the time to start taking good care of the eye area. Apply the remover, blotting it over the surface gently, and then remove it, again gently, with cotton. It will have the additional benefit of removing more mascara than you realized was on your lashes, and prevent the shadowy mascara smudges that often remain after washing or using cream on the face.

## TONING

This is an essential! It is not an extra, or something to do when you have noticed that your skin pores seem large.

After washing with soap, toning the skin with a non-alcohol toning lotion serves a dual purpose. It clears off the soap residue, and firms and closes the surface of the face. This is invaluable in preventing enlarged pores that gather in dirt and other impurities.

It is equally important to use a toning lotion for the same purpose after you cleanse your face with cream, to clear off the cream and makeup residue, and firm and close the skin surface.

*Reminder*: Asian skins, as mentioned before, are sensitive to alcohol and salicylic acid. Check the list of ingredients on the back of products, to prevent breakouts.

If you find yourself without a toning lotion, *witch hazel* (available at drugstores) is a good substitute.

Witch hazel is usually combined with distilled water, as a toning lotion. The reason for specifying distilled water is that it does not

contain impurities. You may also use a cotton pad soaked with tap water, squeezed and then saturated with witch hazel. This dilutes the solution enough to make it safe for the most sensitive skins.

Witch hazel is a useful product to have on your makeup shelf. Aside from being a good toning lotion, it works well in reducing puffy eyelids. Soak two cotton pads in witch hazel, apply one to each eye, and keep them on for five minutes. The puffiness will be reduced. Witch hazel also can help prevent breakout spots, if applied as soon as you feel the spot developing. Apply witch hazel directly to the area four to five times a day. People with oily skins use witch hazel full strength as a skin toner. It is soothing, and a natural way to remove surface oil.

Whether you use a prepared toning lotion or witch hazel, apply with cotton, covering the entire surface of the face and neck. It feels refreshing, as well as producing a clean skin for the next step—a facial pack, or night cream, or a daytime moisturizer. If you haven't been in the habit of using a toner, check your face with a magnifying mirror after one week's use. There will be a noticeable difference—your skin pores will be tight and even.

## RE-SURFACING YOUR SKIN

No matter how old or young you are, or what your skin type is, this is essential at least once a week. Women with oily skins should do it more often. Mature dry skins have lower cell rejuvenation activity, and can be helped by daily or weekly exfoliation. This is a process that removes dead skin cells faster than the skin could do if left on its own. It leaves a smooth, new breathing surface for your face.

There are commercial scruffing or exfoliating creams—containing tiny granules in a creamy base—for you to apply to a clean, wet face and then gently rub in. *Estée Lauder's Gentle Skin Polisher* is one.

Rinse well and feel the difference. Follow this skin-cleansing routine with a moisturizer.

*Reminder:* Salicylic acid is a peeling agent sometimes found in exfoliating products and, as mentioned before, is an ingredient that Asian skins can be sensitive to. Check your product to see what it contains. There are skin polishers that do not contain this acid.

A home face-scruffing preparation that works well is roasted uncooked *oatmeal* (heated in the oven or toaster for one minute) with a bit of lemon peel grated in, plus enough water to make a paste. Rub in gently, rinse thoroughly.

Our dermatologists say that you shouldn't scruff your skin if you have skin breakouts. Blemishes will take longer to heal if the surface of the skin is disturbed.

## OTHER SKIN SURFACE AIDS

Facial packs, whether they are commercial products or home-made, work wonders as temporary refreshers and smoothers.

Facial packs cleanse the pores, firm and tighten skin, stimulate circulation under the skin to reinforce natural cellular activity, and feed the skin surface with moisturizing, nourishing elements.

Oily skins require clay packs, or a deep-cleansing routine before using facial packs. Steaming is the most effective way of opening pores and allowing impurities to be washed out in the natural perspiration that follows. There are steamers designed for this purpose, or you can use a home method. First, wash your face thoroughly. Then boil a pot of water. Remove the pot from the heat and place your face—not too close—over it. Drape a towel over your head to form a curtain around the face and let the steam do its work. Then rinse your face thoroughly and use a toner.

Homemade packs are remarkably effective. They range from a

simple application of cucumber slices, to a recipe for whipping up egg yolks and whites with other ingredients. Here are some for you to try.

Start with a squeaky-clean face, and eye cream applied around the entire eye area. Plan on lying down while these are working on your face. Put your feet up—relax!

Slices of *cucumber* applied to the face, rubbed gently over the surface in a circular motion, is a time-tested skin refresher and pore tightener. Highly soothing, it is an especially pleasant treatment in hot weather.

Juice from the leaves of the *aloe* plant is another effective skin refresher and toner. Keep a plant handy. Take one leaf from the plant and slice in half. With oily skin, apply directly, rubbing the juicy flesh of the plant over the skin surface. With dry or sensitive skin, apply moisturizer first, then rub the juice over the face. Regular users swear that it helps prevent wrinkles.

Both the cucumber and the aloe can be used as quick facial pick-ups in your makeup routine. They require very little time and work immediately.

*Egg whites*, beaten to a froth, are an effective skin tightener and smoother. Oily skins will find them satisfactory used by themselves. Those with dry or sensitive skins can combine the egg whites with other ingredients.

Here are some skin nourishing and smoothing recipes. The simplest one is applying a thin layer of pure *honey* to the face. Another is to beat one *egg yolk* with a few drops of *lemon* juice, and apply that. The third is to mix half an *egg yolk* with one tablespoon of *honey*, add a beaten *egg white*, fold in, and then apply the honey-egg mixture to the face. The ultimate skin-tightener and smoother is one *egg white* beaten up and then applied.

Each of these packs should be left on for ten to fifteen minutes and then washed off. In addition to the recipes mentioned, there are many others that include milk or yogurt. Milk is a natural emulsion of oil in water. These milk-based recipes are also effective and pleasant to use.

Commercial face packs are well-documented as to their skin nourishing and surface smoothing. They, too, require an absolutely clean face, the application of eye cream around the eyes first, and a ten to fifteen minute period of rest while they work. Read the directions before buying and using them. It will be indicated whether they are for dry or oily skin, for deep cleansing, or nourishment, or toning the skin surface.

A facial treatment, which involves massage with creams, and skin stimulation through patting or electric stimulation, will release tension and increase circulation, dilating the blood vessels to bring more oxygen to the skin surface. It is both relaxing and refreshing, but does not have any long-term effects on the skin or the shape of your face.

No matter what kind of facial pack or cleansing you choose to use, it should be followed by a toning lotion. Pat on the toner, and enjoy the feeling of a clean, re-surfaced skin!

## MEDICAL MEASURES FOR THE FACE

Each of the following treatments is done by a professional, a medical doctor, under surgical-clean conditions. Know what the treatment involves—the time period, the precautions you must take— and know your doctor. Remember also that you may heal with more scar tissue than other women because of your skin composition.

**Chemical peeling** is done in the doctor's office. It does not require an anesthetic or hospitalization. Chemical peeling will not remove scars as dermabrasion (explained later) does, but it will improve the texture of the skin and soften small wrinkles so as to make them unnoticeable. A chemical paste is applied to the skin, leaving a sunburned feeling. A soft bandage is applied over the skin for 48 hours and then the skin is powdered and an antibiotic ointment applied. These last two applications soften the crust that has formed, and the crust gradually peels away to reveal the new skin underneath. Allow three weeks to heal, and for the face to return to its natural color. No makeup should be used until the skin has completely healed, and sunning should be avoided for six months.

**Collagen injections** are designed to help those with scarred or aging skin. The direct addition of collagen through a series of local injections under the skin eliminates wrinkles, slight sagging, and also scars. The treatment is one syringe of collagen per visit to the dermatologist, for a total of two or three injections. The effect lasts for three to eighteen months, after which the body absorbs the collagen. The treatment is done in the doctor's office.

**Dermabrasion** is similar to chemical peeling, but requires two to three days' hospitalization, and is done under an anesthetic. It is effective for some scars, especially deep acne scars, and improves aging skin. The top layers of skin are removed, and then the face is protected by a dressing that gradually peels off as the face heals. You cannot wear makeup for three weeks, and you must not sun for three months. If you are using the pill, you must use another method of contraception for one month before, and two months after, the operation, as there is a chance of skin spotting.

**Plastic surgery** is done by a medical doctor who is a specialist in this field. Chin implants and nose shaping, as well as some kinds of eyelid surgery, are some of the treatments that last permanently.

**Eyelid surgery** reshapes the lids and is effective in giving an

eyelid crease, or in removing heaviness in the lids, or opening the eyelid in another way. This surgery can be done in the doctor's office, with a local anesthetic. There is bruising and swelling for about two weeks, and dark glasses have to be worn during that period. No makeup can be worn until the healing period is over.

**Face lifts** require an anesthetic and hospitalization. The time of life when it seems to have best results is when women are in their forties. The effects of a face lift should last for five to ten years. The skin will not stop aging during these years, but the aging lines will have been erased or made less noticeable. There will be swelling and bruising, and stitches will be removed at various times within a two-week period after the operation. The operation takes about two hours. The period of hospitalization depends on what kind of face lift you have had, but at least two or three days are needed, plus the return visits to the doctor for removal of the stitches. Bruises and swelling subside within three weeks, but it is three to six months before the best results are noticed. The idea of a face lift is to remove wrinkles and sagging, without removing the natural expression lines of the face.

*A final word*: Choose your plastic surgeon with care. Tell him what you want and then listen to what he says you can realistically expect.

# 6 MOISTURIZING, FEEDING, AND PROTECTING YOUR SKIN

Let's get into the facts of skin protection. You may not think this is so necessary if you're very young, but it will mean a lot to you in ten years. If you're not so young, it means a great deal right now as well as in the months and years to come.

The smoothness of Asian skin was mentioned earlier. Keep in mind that this is a plus factor which deserves tender care. Smooth, soft skin can become dry if you take it for granted, and do not give it extra care.

## MOISTURIZING

Asian skin, like any other, needs a moisturizer that preserves the moisture that the skin contains, without closing the pores and interfering with the skin's natural breathing ability.

The very first and most important thing to remember for skin health is to apply a moisturizer to *damp* skin. After showering or bathing, don't remove all the water on your skin by too vigorous toweling. While you're still damp, apply a moisturizer to your face and body. This will lock in the surface moisture and help, more than anything else can, to keep your skin cells at a normal moisture level.

Oily skins need moisturizers as much as dry skins do. Moisturizing means water and water retention. It doesn't mean that you are

putting anything greasy on your skin. Use a moisturizer that is especially designed for oily skin. Some of these are mentioned later on in this chapter.

Those with normal skin are likely to have an oily T-zone—the forehead, the nose, and the chin—and should avoid using a moisturizer on this area.

Makeup foundations, soothing as they may feel, do not take the place of a moisturizer. Use a moisturizer first, wait a few minutes, then apply the foundation.

Many of the newer formulas used in night creams that claim to help the skin renew itself do not contain moisturizing elements in adequate amounts for mature skins. Notice that the label instructs you to apply the skin-renewing cream before using a moisturizer. Do as they say!

In mentioning effective moisturizers, our dermatologists stress that a moisturizer need not be expensive. Some of the products are well-known. One of them may be a great surprise to you.

Especially for sensitive skins, it is necessary to have a moisturizing agent that contains no irritants. One of our dermatologists mentions *Lubriderm* as one of these. It is used in hospitals and is available in a generous-sized bottle at a reasonable price. *Keri Lotion* is good. One of the best, which does not cause any kind of breakout, is *Crisco*, the vegetable shortening. *Crisco* has been recommended by three New York dermatologists as an excellent moisturizer. It is remarkably effective when used on a damp skin and is not as greasy as you would expect. *Petrolatum*, or *Vaseline*, is also good for moisturizing a face without causing any irritation, but both of these are likely to feel sticky on the face, unless all the excess is removed.

## FEEDING THE SKIN

Our dermatologists agree that lotions and creams, with their sophisticated chemical ingredients, penetrate the skin through perhaps three layers of skin cells.

This is not reaching deep enough to rejuvenate the skin and make it younger. But it does penetrate sufficiently to aid the skin cells in maintaining normal regenerative activity, and increasing cell renewal when people reach that age where it declines.

Aiding cell activity involves improving the oxygen intake of the skin, and providing help in replacing collagen loss and the loss of elasticity.

Since we are interested here in the surface of the skin, let's go on to what you need to nourish that surface. What you use depends on your age.

All skins need to be kept in good working condition, to be supplied with moisture and to be protected against the environment.

Young skins need a light moisturizer applied over clean, damp skin at night and again in the morning. *Nivea*, *Lubriderm*, and *Keri Lotion* are of this type.

Those who are between twenty-five and thirty-five will find many moisturizers on the market geared to their needs. *Lancome's Bienfait du Matin* is one that also contains vitamins and a sunscreen, a sunscreen being important in skin protection, as we discuss later in this chapter. Those with oily skins have a number to choose from. *Elizabeth Arden's Texturizing Lotion* is one, and *Revlon's Fresh Blotting Lotion* is another.

After thirty-five, it is time to consider using the skin creams that provide more food to increase skin cell renewal. In mature skin, the skin cells do not renew themselves quickly. This results in loss of

skin tone, in wrinkles and sagging, due to less elasticity in the skin, and a need for more moisture. A night cream that contains collagen (a protein complex), elastin (highly elastic fibers that give skin and muscle tissue their elasticity), and RNA (a complex compound that functions in cellular protein synthesis and improves the oxygen intake of the skin) will help in skin renewal. A lighter cream with these properties should be used under daytime makeup. *Lancome's Nutribel* can be used both night and day, *Estée Lauder's European Performance Cream* is another that is a night cream, and the *La Prairie* night and day creams are others among these supercharged skin products.

Left to the last, but very important, is eye cream. Use it *every* night, and *every* morning, by applying it gently over the lid and around the socket, then wait a bit before doing your eye makeup. Surprisingly, older women, who need this cream the most, use it less than the thirty-year-olds who are likely to regard it as a major necessity. A night cream, and daytime moisturizer, don't take its place. The tender skin of the eyelid has a slightly different surface—no pores—and it takes a special cream designed for eyelid use to really show results. Asian eyes don't wrinkle in the same way that Caucasian eyelids do, but they do lose their elasticity and droop, and the surrounding character wrinkles are the same. If eye cream is not part of your routine, be sure to include it.

## FROM THE INSIDE

Getting enough sleep is the most simple and basic thing that you can do for your skin care. The skin renews itself, building new skin cells, while the body is sleeping. Insufficient sleep will lead to tired-looking skin and a tired-looking face. Sleeping enough hours each night is the first step in having healthy skin.

Drinking six to eight glasses of water a day is another easy way to improve your skin condition.

The food you eat—and the vitamins, minerals, and fats it provides—is what your body needs to function. Getting these from natural sources, and some come *only* from natural sources, is more desirable than taking a bundle of pills. Include vegetables or fruit, bread or a cereal, dairy products, and meat, poultry, or fish at every meal.

The importance of a balanced diet cannot be stressed enough. There is an interaction between different elements in a balanced diet. For instance, in order for the body to be able to absorb a certain mineral, it might be necessary to have a certain vitamin. This is a drastic simpification of a complicated subject, and the reason that balance is emphasized in a good diet.

Asian skin and hair, in their Asian environment, are greatly affected by a diet that includes fish, a prime source of vitamin E, proteins, and minerals. Sardines are particularly high in all three of these elements that are helpful in maintaining healthy skin and hair.

Dr. Kiyoshi Toda, head of dermatology at Tokyo Teishin Hospital, emphasized the importance of including fish in a diet to have glossy hair and healthy skin. He said that some vegetables—carrots, squash, and tomatoes in particular—contain beta-carotene, which the liver transforms into vitamin A. Vitamin A helps in protecting the skin against sun damage, an important consideration for everyone.

## PROTECTION AGAINST THE SUN

Your skin's greatest enemy is the sun. It's marvelous to have a glowing tan, but how you achieve this—if you want it—is terribly important. If you don't want it—if you like the pale, pearly look instead—it is equally important to know how to get protection.

## Protection in Warmer Climates

You've read in a previous chapter about the melanin content of your skin, and the need for more thoughtful protection than lighter-skinned people use. Remember that the darker shade of your skin does not mean that you are safe from harmful ultraviolet rays.

Walking down the street, playing tennis, biking, or any outdoor activity in a warm climate brings a need for skin protection. Remember also that cloudy days do not mean that you cannot get tanned or burned. It is necessary to use some type of sunscreen every day.

There are oil-free sun shields and blocks to wear under makeup. It isn't necessary to use a preparation that is greasy. For everyday use there are makeup foundations that include a sunscreening agent. *Clinique's Continuous Coverage* contains a sun block for complete protection. Check product labels until you find a sunscreening agent that is right for you—to wear over a moisturized skin, or under foundation, or for oily skin.

When your favorite foundation doesn't have a sunscreening capability, use a non-greasy protective cream first, applying it after toning your skin.

For active sports and sunbathing, go straight to the sunscreens that contain PABA (para amino benzoic acid), an important protective agent against ultraviolet rays. These sunscreens are numbered according to their degree of protection. For instance, SPF (skin protection factor) #2 will allow you to stay in the sun, without burning, twice as long as you could with a bare skin. It is the minimum amount of protection and should be used only when your skin already has a protective tan.

For beginning a tan, use a #15 or #12. It provides first-day protection, and gives your skin a chance to adapt to the sun's hazardous rays. You should use three numbers—the first for maximum protec-

tion, the second numbered 8 or 6 for medium protection, and the third, a minimum sunscreen numbered 6 or 2 for the time when your skin has developed its protective shield.

## Protection in Transition

In going to a high altitude for skiing, or from a winter climate to a warm, sunny one, stay with the *maximum* protection until you've used up the tube or bottle. The shock to your skin may not be particularly noticeable to you, but dermatologists with microscopic slides of the skin surface could show you how immediately and violently the skin reacts. The undulating, surface of ups and downs of normal skin can turn into a surface that looks like satellite photos of the moon's outer crust—cracked, puffy and scaly.

In addition to protecting your skin from excessive ultraviolet rays, sunscreen products seal in the natural skin moisture while still allowing the skin to breathe through open pores.

If you're on the pill, or if you're over 45, you'll need to be particularly careful about exposing your skin to the sun. Being on the pill causes extra sensitivity in some people, as can other medicines (such as sulfa, tetracycline, and tranquilizers) in the form of small brown spotting on the skin surface.

The skin becomes thinner, and needs extra protection, as women get older. Re-evaluate the kind of sun protection you have found effective in the past, and use more than before, to ensure that your changing skin requirements are being met.

## Protection in Cooler Climates

Living in a cooler climate doesn't mean you don't have to worry about protecting yourself from the sun. Find the product that is geared to your geographical zone. If you live in a climate where getting a tan is not easy (or if tanning for you takes time), you may want to consider a sun lamp. Sun lamps can give a good pre-holiday glow, a start on looking tanned. But remember that the tan you achieve with a sun lamp is not a thickening of the skin, as happens with a natural sun tan. Don't use a sun lamp year-round, and don't sunbathe on the same day that you have used a sun lamp. When you do use one, always wear the dark goggles provided, or buy your own. They filter out rays that are harmful to the eyes, and are absolutely necessary.

If you are taking any medication, check with your doctor before using the lamp, as there may be a sunburn reaction caused by certain drugs. Those on the pill may find that there is some brown spotting of the skin. Always shower before using a sun lamp, since some cosmetics or perfumes contain oils that can produce excessive burning, or tanning in patches. Remember, sun lamps darken the skin, but do not give it protection against the sun. Start sunbathing with highly protective sunscreeners.

## PROTECTION AGAINST THE ENVIRONMENT

Both sunscreens and moisturizers form a protective layer on the face and body that aids in guarding against other environmental hazards, such as pollution and dust, that can affect the skin.

Humidity in the atmosphere is of much benefit to the skin, hair, and nasal passages. Bear this in mind if you live in a cold or dry climate. House plants increase the humidity in the air, as does putting a bowl of water on the radiator. The most effective way of coping with dry air is to use an electric humidifier.

The best way to minimize the effects of harmful environmental conditions is to keep your skin clean and healthy. Get enough sleep, eat the right foods, and protect your skin to keep it in tip-top shape.

# 7 YOUR FOUNDATION

## TYPES, AND HOW TO CHOOSE THEM

The kind of foundation you use—a cream or emulsion, a gel or water-based preparation—depends on the texture and condition of your skin.

The total effect of your face—an effect ranging from natural to highly dramatic—is not dependent on the foundation you wear, but on the coloring techniques that will be explained in the next chapters.

Young skins that are prone to breakouts, and all oily skins, should use a preparation designed especially for oily skin. This kind of foundation provides a smooth matte surface and does not add surface oil. *Clinque's Pore Minimizer Makeup* is one.

Makeup expert Arthur Scott specializes in photography and TV commercials. He does the *Chanel* commercials, and his makeup work is seen in Italian *Vogue* and other high-fashion magazines. He also makes up individuals for special events. He is thoroughly familiar with working with less-than-perfect faces, which means that he uses constructive techniques to improve features. Scott uses *Estée Lauder's Fresh Air Foundation*, a water-based preparation, for oily skins. This should not be confused with the kind of cake foundation that is applied with water and a sponge, and is also water-based.

Scott warns that pancake foundation is aging for mature skins and makes any skin look very flat. "I use it only for body makeup," Scott says.

Gels are transparent, non-greasy, color coverings, giving a natural look, with the texture of the skin showing through. Becoming more popular because of its light transparency of color, and the natural look it provides, a gel foundation produces a basic daytime sports look. None of the contouring that provides highs and lows, and visual interest on the surface of the face, can be done over this transparent film. "You have to be eighteen years old, or have flawless skin, to use a gel," says Scott, with photography in mind.

An emulsion is a foundation that can be poured, or squeezed freely from a tube, a moisturizing cover that feels light on the face. It is popular with young women, as well as those approaching their forties.

People with dry skins, or those with mature skin, should use an oil-based cream foundation. It will moisturize your skin. This kind of foundation has an elasticity which keeps it from cracking or settling into wrinkles. "Use an oil-based cream if you're not young," Scott advises. "Water-based preparations have an aging effect on dry skin, or skin that has wrinkles."

Check the product labels, to know exactly what you are about to put on your face.

*To keep in mind*: Christian Dior's creative artist Tyen, who is Vietnamese, and who works in Paris to design Dior's new colors and cosmetic image each season, says, "I don't understand why Asian women wear so much foundation, so heavy. They have beautiful skins, and they cover them so that they can't be seen. The beauty of the skin should be seen." Lighter coverage is better—lighter in texture—say both Scott and Tyen.

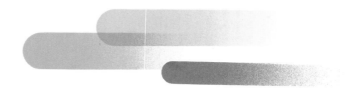

## THE COLOR OF YOUR FOUNDATION

Choose your foundation to match your skin color. There should be no difference in color between your face and neck, and also your face and hands.

"Women put their hands to their face a lot, to arrange their hair, or while they're talking. It looks terrible to see a completely different color on the face. And be careful not to use a lighter color; it looks like a mask," New York makeup expert Arthur Scott advises.

Remember that you will be applying additional color over the foundation, when you do your facial contouring and add blusher. The foundation color is not necessarily the color that will be most noticeable on your face.

How can you be sure to match your skin color? "Test a foundation on the inside of your wrist or arm. That's the area where the sun doesn't change your skin color," says Scott. This area is the same color as the natural coloring of your face. Scott warns that stores often have fluorescent lighting that removes a pink tint from the foundation, and gives a color effect that is different from what is seen in natural lighting or daylight. If possible, go to a door or window, to check the foundation color in natural light. It may be pinker than under the store lights.

Our makeup experts agree that the best color choices for Asian skin are in the beige range—from ivory beige on through to sunny or medium beige—depending on your skin color. "Don't go for a pinkish tone," warns Scott, "it doesn't look good on women with Asian skin." Our women with Asian features, who have given their beauty regimes at the end of this book, agree almost unanimously on this.

## Undercolors

It is possible to use a control color (also called primer) under the foundation. A green undercoating takes out ruddiness, patches of red, from the face. A violet undercoating removes sallowness, makes the skin look whiter. A pink undercoating is popular in Asia where it is thought to give a pale glow. Under-foundation colors are becoming more familiar in Western countries. Some products that will tone down the yellowish hue of Asian skin are *Estée Lauder Undercolor Mauve Color Primer* and *Merle Norman Lilac Mist Color Mist*. Unless there is a specific need to even out the complexion color you may prefer a veiling of colored powder over the foundation.

*Note*: If you wear glasses, avoid yellow frames or frames with yellow overtones. The yellow color will intensify the sallow color of Asian skin.

## APPLYING YOUR FOUNDATION

Over a cleansed, toned, and moisturized face, the foundation is truly that, the first step in building a face look. Makeup expert Scott does his contouring before using a foundation, since it gives a more subtle effect for photography, but he says that using the foundation first, and then contouring over it, is much easier for non-professionals.

When using a water-based preparation, shake it, pour a spoonful into the palm of your hand, and then apply quickly to the face. Smooth it out from each cheek to the hairline, then over the nose and mouth and chin. Smooth more over the forehead and down to the cheeks. Be sure to blend the foundation over the entire jaw, and down into the neck area. Remember to wash your hands before applying the foundation.

Kimi Oshiro, the Shiseido makeup expert who does the faces of both Caucasians and Asians for designer fashion shows in Paris, uses a sponge to smooth the foundation on, as does Scott. Scott recommends, when using a cream foundation, that "you put a dot of the cream on the forehead, each cheek, and the chin, then smooth over the entire surface. Go over the jaw, blending it into the neck area."

It is remarkable how little of the actual foundation these experts use. They achieve smooth coverage with a very small amount of foundation. Both mention that it is absolutely necessary to be meticulous about rinsing out the sponge after each use. Don't allow a buildup of foundation to remain in the facial sponge. If you do, bacteria will form.

Now you're ready for contouring.

# 8 CONTOURING
## *The Important Technique*

"There's more you can do with the Asian face to create areas of light and dark, and to make hollows and high points for visual interest," says Kimi Oshiro, Shiseido's creative makeup expert who designs the facial images for Paris fashion shows by Lanvin, Kenzo, Thierry Mugler, Issey Miyake, and others.

Showing the different planes of the face, the ups and downs of the surface, is the important fundamental step in making up the Asian face. The basic contouring that is right for you will be the same whether you are aiming for all-out glamour or a more subdued look.

You will be using a face-shader, a shading stick, or a powder or foundation that is two shades darker than what is on your face now. Any one of these contouring aids will create areas that recede.

You will also be using a highlighter. The easiest one to use is white eyeshadow powder. A very light concealer stick is also effective.

These two contouring aids—the darker one for making areas recede, the lighter one for highlighting—will create highs and lows on your face, giving it visual interest, by breaking up the flat plane that is a characteristic of Asian faces. These two tools will also be used to make your weak points less obvious, your strong points more striking.

Contouring your face is easy, but it takes practice. You have to

know your face first, and you have to blend the edges of the darker area carefully. Remember that when you blend out, more of the area will be covered than you may have expected.

Oshiro uses *Shiseido's Face-shader* (not yet available outside Japan) in a taupe-gray-brown color. Makeup expert Arthur Scott uses *Shiseido's Moisture Mist Foundation* in a roll-up stick, two shades darker than the foundation he is working on. *Calvin Klein Cocoa Contouring Powder* is another product you can use. Most makeup experts agree that a foundation two shades darker than what is used on the face will give a good, subtle shading. In a pinch, a light gray-brown eyeshadow should work.

All of our makeup experts stress that the most important thing to remember about contouring is to blend the edges of the darker areas into the foundation, so that there is no distinct shadow. Blend, blend, blend, is the word that is used most often in describing contouring. Use the finger to smooth and blend the edges of the contouring powder or stick so that there is no distinguishable difference between the contour color and the foundation.

## WHAT THE CONTOUR SHADER DOES

How is the shader used? To minimize a jaw that is too angular or too

wide, to form interesting hollows beneath cheekbones, to round off a prominent cheekbone, to narrow and define a nose, to make a prominent chin recede, to deemphasize a high forehead, or to use under a double chin.

The highlighter is used to lengthen a short nose, to bring forward a receding chin, to distract the eye from a weak point and focus it somewhere else.

Once you understand this fact—that the shadow goes where you don't want anything protruding, and the highlighter goes where you do want something to protrude—you can work on your individual look without having to check charts of the face.

Know your face. Study it in a three-way mirror, so that you will see yourself as others see you, from the side in profile, as well as from the front. Use a hand mirror if a three-way mirror isn't available.

Is your jaw heavy at the side, or too angular? Does your chin stick out? Would you like to make your nose less broad? Do you think that your eyes protrude too much? Would you like an interesting hollow under your cheekbone? Do you want your face to curve around to the hairline?

Face-shading forms, or improves, these features.

# THE BASIC CONTOURING

One of the characteristics of the Asian face is that it is flat. It therefore needs highs and lows. The following three contouring steps are recommended to give your face these highs and lows. Experts do these three steps to everyone, before taking individual features into consideration.

*For Everyone*

**THE EYES.** (Figure 1.) Apply the shader to the area above the eyelashes, and continue it up to the eyebrow. Do this by placing a dot of the shader above each eye, then blend. Cover the area from the side of the nose, darken the side of the bridge of the nose, and carry the shading out and up to the eyebrow. Fade it across to the temple at the end of the eyebrow.

This technique is the exact opposite of what is done for eyes with other racial characteristics. It defines the bridge of the nose by making the sides of the nose darker. It makes the area above the eyelashes up to the eyebrow recede and prepares this area for color.

**THE CHIN.** (Figure 2.) Apply a dot of shader under the lower lip, and blend it into a triangle pointing toward the chin. This gives a look of indentation below the mouth, and is part of creating highs and lows.

**THE SIDES OF THE FACE.** (Figure 3.) Apply the shader to each side of the face at the hairline. Japanese television makeup people do this to everyone. Take the shader from just below the temples—at eye level—down each side of the face to the jawline, and over the angle of the corner of the jaw.

This makes the face look as if it curves inward toward the hairline, giving a rounded effect, rather than having the face look as if it were on one plane.

Fig. 1.

Fig. 2.

Fig. 3.

**FOR CHEEK HOLLOWS.** (Figure 4.) If you need to define a hollow at the side of your cheek, and you probably do need this, place a triangle of shader under the outer part of the cheekbone, pointing toward the hairline.

Makeup artist Scott warns against putting cheek hollows on an older face. "Mature faces are more angular than young faces. They don't need this."

**FOR YOUR JAW.** (Figure 5.) If your jaw seems a bit heavy at the sides of the chin, shade over this little bulge, continuing the shading down onto the underjaw. Remember to blend!

Fig. 4.

Fig. 5.

**FOR A PROTRUDING CHIN.** (Figure 6.) Do the same kind of shading, placing a bit of shader at the edge of the chin, and blending it over the edge and back onto the lower jaw. This will keep it from looking prominent.

**FOR A DOUBLE CHIN.** (Figure 7.) Blend the shader across the underneath of the chin in the front, tailing it off at each side of the bulge.

This makes the double chin less prominent, and is especially effective from the side. Use your three-way mirror, or your hand mirror, and see the difference!

Fig. 6.

Fig. 7.

**FOR A BROAD NOSE.** (Figure 8.) Take the shader down on each side of the nose in a narrow line, then blend. It creates shadows that narrow the nose.

**FOR A NOSE THAT CURVES DOWN AT THE END.** (Figure 9.) Place shadow on the tip of the nose and blend.

*Note*: It is very difficult to do any more nose shaping than narrowing, lifting the bridge, and highlighting the tip of the nose or making it recede. Any more than this is accomplished by placing color on other parts of the face to attract the eye there. Emphasize your eye colors, put a bit of blusher above each eyebrow and on the temples. Use pale shades of lipstick that do not draw attention to the mouth and the nose.

Fig. 8.

Fig. 9.

**FOR A JAW THAT IS TOO HEAVY AT THE SIDES OF THE FACE.**
(Figure 10.) Place the shader down the part that is too wide, blending it over the edge and down onto the underjaw. Think of an oval face, and shade that part where your facial lines are outside the oval at the jaw.

**FOR A FOREHEAD THAT IS TOO PROMINENT.** (Figure 11.) If your forehead seems to bulge out, spread the contour shader across the forehead from side to side, blend.

Fig. 10.

Fig. 11.

**FOR A FOREHEAD THAT IS TOO HIGH.** (Figure 12.) Apply a band of shader across the forehead from one side to the other.

**FOR A LONG FACE.** (Figure 13.) Dot a bit of shader on the chin bone and blend. The rest of the illusion is done with blusher, in bands across the face, high on the cheekbones and out, and across the forehead.

**FOR PROMINENT CHEEKBONES.** (Figure 14.) If your cheekbones seem to be the widest part of your face, with the cheek curving in abruptly below them, place your shader along the highest part, in a curve from the outside of the face at the top, in toward the nostril.

**FOR BULGING CHEEKS.** (Figure 15.) If, from the side view, your cheeks bulge out too much, place shader on the bulge, checking it from your side profile.

Fig. 12.

Fig. 13.

Fig. 14.

Fig. 15.

**FOR A ROUND FACE WITH WIDE CHEEKS.** (Figure 16.) Place the shader in dots that form a V shape, across the cheekbone to the point of the V at the temple, then up and back over the eyebrow to the center of the eyebrow. Blend carefully. Evaluate. If it doesn't seem right, use blusher instead, sweeping on color instead of shader.

Almost all of this has been to make areas recede, by making them darker. If your face has large areas of dark, you have applied too much, or not realized that the blending would spread the shadow over a larger area.

Now you will use the highlighter to define these areas further. This is done with a white or ivory cream by makeup professionals, but a white eyeshadow or a very light concealer will work well.

**TO FURTHER NARROW THE NOSE.** (Figure 17.) Put little dots of highlighter down the exact middle of the nose, and blend them in. It will raise the nose, and in combination with the shadow at each side of the nose, you will see a re-shaping that is effective.

**TO LIFT THE BRIDGE OF THE NOSE.** (Figure 18.) On the bridge of the nose, between the eyes, place a tiny bit of white and blend it in.

Fig. 16.

Fig. 17.

Fig. 18.

**FOR A LOW FOREHEAD.** (Figure 19.) Place a line of highlighter down the exact middle from the hairline to the nose, and blend. It's an optical illusion, the white seeming to make that space longer.

**FOR A NARROW OR FLAT FOREHEAD.** (Figure 20.) Place highlighter along the edge of the hairline from the point above the end of one eyebrow up and around and down to the same point on the opposite side. Place a bit of shader on each temple and blend. Then use the palest possible band of highlighter across the forehead from side to side.

*Remember*: The classic shape of the face is an oval. Check your outline, and use contouring where the edges extend beyond an oval shape.

Take a good look at what you've done. Unless you are remarkably skillful, and have done a beautiful job of face contouring, take your makeup off and start again! Note where you have applied too much, or have covered too wide an area. Do it again with a lighter hand. It will go more quickly. You'll look the way you want—the best features highlighted, the others faded away.

**FOR A FINISHING TOUCH.** (Figure 21.) From under the eye out and up to the temple, add a dusting of white powder to give surface interest, and to highlight the eye coloring that you will be doing next.

Set the face with a dusting of translucent powder. Use a powder brush, not a puff. It will make a noticeable difference to the overall effect. Knock the excess powder off the brush, then dust the entire face lightly, beginning with the forehead, then the nose, and picking up more powder on the brush if necessary. Continue until the entire surface, including the lips, is covered. Then brush more, smoothing the powder as you brush off the excess.

*Note:* For mature faces. Do not use face powder under the eyes. It will settle into wrinkles.

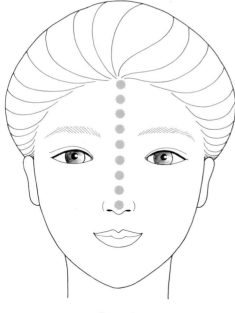

Fig. 19.

Fig. 20.

Fig. 21.

# 9 YOUR EYES
*Shaping with Color*

Asian eyes have advantages when it comes to eyeshadowing. They have a clear space between the upper lid and the brow, an open space that makes layering bands, or triangles, of color easy. There's no crease to cope with, and the orbital bone, the bone above the eye, does not protrude as it does in other eyes.

Because the eyeshadowing is not concealed behind lashes, or in a crease, the colors you use are more apparent. And because these colors are up front, they need to be subtle. Asian eyes require a much more subtle use of color—a consensus of opinion from our makeup experts and our group of women whose makeup techniques are featured in the last chapter of this book.

This shadowing of Asian eyes is a combination of lights and darks, to provide eyelid interest, to *contour* the eye socket, as you contoured your facial planes in the previous chapter.

Check the color of the clothes that you'll be wearing, or the earrings, before deciding on what color scheme you'll use for your eyes. It's very important to echo the earring coloring in the eye coloring!

As the eye coloring techniques are explained, you'll notice that a color choice is given in some cases. The technique will mention blue or green, for instance. If you are wearing green earrings, be

sure that you choose the green instead of the blue. If the technique uses salmon pink, which is a color that goes with most reds, except the very clear shades of scarlet, and you are wearing scarlet, change this salmon pink to a clear coral.

You'll be doing a lot of thinking, in evaluating the eye color techniques explained here. While doing so, think of the colors you particularly like to wear when studying the daytime techniques, or a certain outfit that you want to wear in the evening, when you're considering evening techniques.

The colors you use are most important. To say a color should be subtle is easy. The only way you can judge the colors that are best for your eyes is by trying these colors on your skin. Use the inside of your wrist as a testing area. The skin there is your natural color, nearest to your eyelid color. See whether the shade of green turns muddy, or brightens the skin. Experiment with putting one color over another. Test for the eyeshadow's ability to stick well on the skin, and to spread smoothly.

"Don't use a liquid eyeliner," say makeup artists Kimi Oshiro and Arthur Scott. Their opinion is that it gives a hard look that is distinctly unflattering.

You'll be using eyeliner pencils, plus soft-center eye pencils that will smudge easily, or eyeshadow powders or creams. Since make-up artists agree on using two to four colors on the lids, you may find it easier to use eyeshadow cake powders when first developing a new eyecoloring technique. You'll need cotton buds, little sticks with cotton-wrapped ends, to use for smudging.

Read through the Daytime Techniques, check the illustration for each one, and then choose the look that you'll experiment with first.

Lining the eye is important. Lining the eye to define it and add brilliance to the eye is so important that some professional athletes have their lashlines tattooed dark, in order to look their best when being photographed. Dr. Carole Shear mentioned this when asked if an eyeliner pencil used inside the lashline is safe for the eye. "The eye washes out any irritants," she said, noting that what causes eye infections is using dirty sponge applicators or brushes, or allowing someone else to use your makeup applicators and then re-using them yourself.

The Vietnamese makeup expert Tyen, who creates the new Christian Dior cosmetic images states frankly, "There is no way to make Asian eyes look large or round. They aren't. They should be made to look longer, to extend farther out, to make them more interesting, and they should be colored subtly, with a combination of colors. Asian eyes are beautiful."

## DAYTIME EYESHADING TECHNIQUES

In the last chapter we mentioned putting the contouring shader over the entire eye socket. This is a preparation for both daytime and evening looks.

Keep your eyeliner pencils sharpened! Dull points are hard to use accurately.

*Daytime Technique 1*. (Figure 1.) The most basic daytime look is to use a dark brown eyeliner pencil on both the upper and lower lids, taking each line past the outer corner of the eye, and filling in with brown or white the little triangle that is formed at the corner of the outer eye. Brush across the area above the eye with brown shadow. Have it darker toward the nose, and darker above the outer edge of the eyelid. Carry it past the corner of the eye, blending it off. Lighten it as it goes up, but keep it dark near the lashline. Place a dab of blue (or green) shadow at the highest point of the eyeball (in the middle) and blend its edges.

Dark brown eyeliner pencil gives a softer look to the eye than a black pencil does.

Fig. 1.

*Daytime Technique 2*. (Figure 2.) The second basic daytime look uses a dark brown eyeliner pencil for the lower lid, and a navy blue pencil to line the upper lid. Purple-lavender eyeshadow is used above the eye in the same way as in Technique 1. A dab of green goes on the center of the eyeball, and is blended.
*Note:* To open the eye (Figure 3), use a bit more eyeliner at the very center of the upper lid, doming it up in a tiny mound above the lash-line. This results in a stronger eye look, especially when used with Technique 2.

Fig. 2.

Fig. 3.

A variation in eyelining is just the opposite (Figure 4). Line the inside and outside corners of the eyes with dark brown, leaving the center of the lid bare. Fill in the center with blue (or green) eyeliner for both upper and lower lids. This kind of lid-lining gives emphasis to the center of the eye also.

Both the brown eyeshadowing, and the purple-lavender shading, should be darker at both ends than in the middle, a contouring trick used repeatedly in the previous chapter. What is colored dark will recede, what is lighter will come forward. This technique of using a lighter shade, or different color, for the center of the eyeball, contours this area to give the eye a rounded look.

Fig. 4.

*Daytime Technique 3*. (Figure 5.) Use a dark blue eyeliner pencil to line the lower lid, carrying the line past the corner of the eye. Using a dark brown eyeliner, line the upper lid in the same way. Fill in the little triangle that forms at the outer corner, using a brown or white pencil.

Those who have a double-fold eyelid, fill in the area between the lashline and the second line with a purple eyeliner. A double-fold lid is one which has a second line above the lashline, or above part of the lashline.

Using a mauve (combination of purple, lightened with gray and blue) eyeshadow, cover the eyelid three-quarters of the way up to the brow. Do it in a triangle that sits over the outer two-thirds of the eye, the narrowest part of the triangle being near the nose. Keep the color darkest at the lashline and out to the edge that extends slightly beyond the eye corner. Smudge it to lighten this mauve color as it goes up and out. Round it off. Use a light gray eye pencil and make a line on the lower lid between the lashline and the eye. You may find that this opens the eye further. Place a dab of teal green, or plum red, in the center of the eye socket, at the highest part of the eyeball, and blend gently.

This mauve shadow over the lid is well worth trying. Not as quiet as brown, not as bold as purple, it gives a good look.

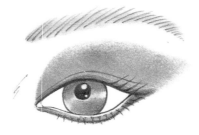

Fig. 5.

*Daytime Technique 4.* (Figure 6.) Layering the shadows. This is slightly more vivid than the other daytime looks, a late day-into-evening eye makeup. You'll be using three stripes of color across the eye socket. Line the lids with dark blue, taking the lines past the outer corner of the eye, as you did in the other techniques. Fill in the triangle that forms with dark blue. The color that you put above the eyelid is purple, smudged across in a band. The middle level is the charcoal or navy shade. The band of color under the brow is yellow-gold. Each layer is patted to blend in with the one next to it.

Fig. 6.

**_Daytime Technique 5._** (Figure 7.) If you love the look of blue, line the eyes with navy, in the same way as mentioned in the other techniques. Use dark gray under the lower lid, narrow at the middle of the eye, wider to the outer edge and beyond. Use the same dark gray over the upper lid, extending it out to meet the lower line. Fill in the shadow triangle with gray. Shade blue shadow over the rest of your eye, paling it up to under the brow.

**_Daytime Technique 6._** (Figure 8.) If your eyes are close-set, use the same methods of coloring, as suggested in the combinations above but put liner only on the outer two-thirds of each lid. The shadowing above the liner will be palest at the middle as before, but it will be darkest above the outer half of your eye.

Fig. 7.

Fig. 8.

***Daytime Technique 7.*** (Figure 9.) To make bulging eyes recede into the eye socket, use your dark brown eyeliner as before. Use dark brown or gray shadow above the upper lid in a curve that pales at the outer part, under the brow. Put a crescent of highlighter over the socket under the outer part of the brow. Put another crescent shape of highlighter under the lower lid.

Fig. 9.

***Daytime Technique 8.*** (Figure 10.) Kimi Oshiro of Shiseido suggests using a strong purple eye pencil to draw a crease shadow across the eye socket area. Decide where on the lid you would like it to be (halfway between the lid and the brow is usual). Draw a crease in purple, taking it in an arch all the way across the lid. Smudge it a bit.

Fig. 10.

***Daytime Technique 9.*** (Figure 11.) Take a golden yellow eyeshadow, and put a flick of it under the brow, smudging it along to the end of the brow. It molds the areas of lights and darks, contrasting with the mauve or brown shadow that covers the rest of the lid. Tyen of Christian Dior says that yellow eyeshadow looks good on Asian eyes. "Women don't want to use it because there are yellow tones under the skin, and they think the yellow shadow will accent this. It doesn't. It looks very good."

Fig. 11.

Using this same yellow shadow, put a dab of it on the highest part of the eyeball, at the middle of the area between lash and brow (Figure 12). Arthur Scott suggests this as another way of highlighting the eye and adding visual interest.

Fig. 12.

***Daytime Technique 10.*** (Figure 13.) Another variation is to add a light stroke of lipstick on the orbital bone, and blend. Put the thin line parallel to, and below, the eyebrow arch and the brow end.

Fig. 13.

***Daytime Technique 11.*** (Figure 14.) Another good look is acquired by using the eyeshadow on the upper part of the lid, and leaving the lower part, just above the lashline, without shadowing, or with a much lighter color. For instance, use a purple brown at top, then put a light lavender just above the lids.

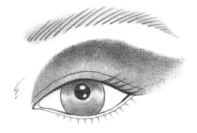

Fig. 14.

***Daytime Technique 12.*** (Figure 15.) An eye-opening tip is to use a very light shade, a pale blue or pale green, in the little fold that appears above the eye. If you don't have a fold, use this pale color anyway—try the effect.

Fig. 15.

*Finishing the look.* An eyelash curler is necessary. Use light pressure along the lashes at two different points to coax a curve. Don't clamp the curler on the lashes at one spot.

Mascara brightens the eye. For daytime, use black mascara. Makeup expert Arthur Scott says to get the mascara as close to the roots of the lashes as possible. "Get it in there, and whip it out," brushing out and up. Brush along the tips of the lower lashes, from side to side.

*Evaluate.* Your goal is to make your eyes look brighter, with a soft frame of color. The total effect should be one of soft darks, with emphasis on *soft.* Too much dark will weigh down the brilliance of the eye itself. Notice that nowhere has black been mentioned in eye-coloring. Black has the effect of dulling the eye if used over a large expanse of the area. It will also make your eyes look smaller.

If your eyes appear to be a mass of color, take the makeup off, re-think the amount of coloring you will apply, and start over.

Says Christian Dior's Tyen, "In the daytime, make up at a window. Get a natural light. Neon light, fluorescent light, takes the color out of the skin, and then people put on too much color. When they go out the look is not right."

Practice! The coloring techniques get easier to use. Leave out what you think is unnecessary for your daytime look.

Eye makeup for evening is a matter of adding color and intensifying color. Arthur Scott advises strongly against the use of shiny eyeshadow, since he says that this will spoil the contouring that you have accomplished with the layering of shadows and highlights. "Intensify the eye colors, increase what is already done for daytime," Scott says.

*Evening Technique 1.* (Figure 16.) The quiet evening look. Line the eyes in navy blue, carrying each lashline out beyond the eye, and filling in the triangle. Remember the triangle of mauve eyeshadow you used in the daytime? Make a bigger triangle, covering more of the same area.

Take a second color of shadow, and apply it over part of the mauve triangle, next to the lid. It will be like laying a smaller triangle over the first one. The color to be used? Some like the effect of a dark color, like a plum red, while others prefer the brighter lighter contrast of teal (blue-green).

Smudge this extra shadow carefully, taking it beyond the eye and up, and then blending off the edges.

When you use the dark shadow, be sure to use the light yellow under the brow, and on the highest part of the eye socket. This provides visual balance, and an effective brightening.

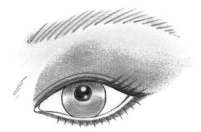

Fig. 16.

*Evening Technique 2.* (Figure 17.) Line the eyes with navy. Using the same brown eyeshadow as in the daytime eye, cover the eye socket, and also ring the area under the lower lid. Apply pink on the area above the lashline of the inner eye, and light blue over the middle of the eye, leaving the outer part brown. The pink, and the blue, extend almost halfway up to the brow. Add ivory highlighting powder under the brow, from halfway out, deepening it toward the eye, and encircling the eye.

Fig. 17.

*Evening Technique 3.* (Figure 18.) Line the eyes with navy blue. Then take a medium blue and cover the area above the lid, to about one-third up, taking the blue out to a point beyond the end of the eyebrow. Using the same blue, start halfway along the lower lid, and take this blue out to meet the other shadow. Fill in the triangle. Cover the entire area from the eyebrow down to the blue, using salmon pink.

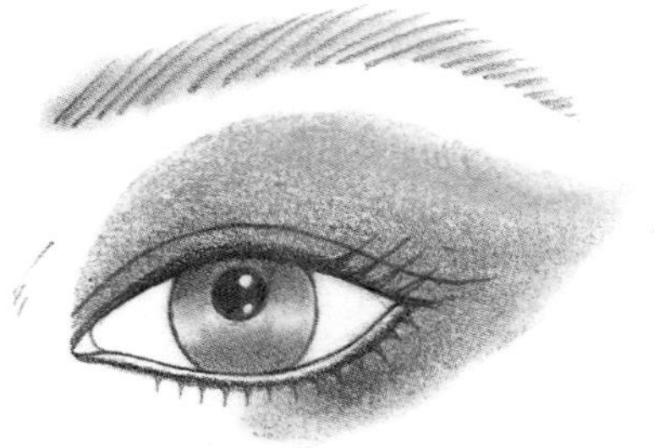

Fig. 18.

*Evening Technique 4.* (Figure 19.) Line the lids with navy. Add salmon pink to a small part of the upper eyelid near the nose. Add more salmon pink at the outer corner. Fill in the rest of the area with medium blue in a wing shape, fading out just below the brow. Line under the brow with the white highlighter.

Fig. 19.

*Evening Technique 5.* (Figure 20.) For an evening eye that is distinctly stylish! Line the lids with navy. Add a wedge of medium blue (or green) above the upper lashes from the inside corner of the eye narrowing out to a line at the outer corner. Add a narrow shading of blue (or green) under the lower lid, two-thirds of the way toward the outer corner. Carry this out beyond the eye. Now put a band of yellow gold above the blue (or green) of the upper lid. Color it out to beyond the end of the eyebrow in a lift starting from the outer corner of the eye. Put peach pink above this, under the brow, starting from the side of the bridge of the nose.

Fig. 20.

*Evening Technique 6.* (Figure 21.) Line the outer half of the top lid, up to the brow, with a golden bronze. Cover the eye socket completely with nut brown. Highlight the inner corner just below the center of the brow with a frosty peach.

Fig. 21.

*Evening Technique 7.* (Figure 22.) For a dramatic look. Take your favorite color—purple or green or medium blue or even one of the pretty pale shades—and make a broad stroke across your eyeball, from above the inner eye out beyond the end of the eye. Do it like a brush stroke, keeping it close to the lashes, and let the color fade at the top of the stroke.

Fig. 22.

*Extra eyelashes.* This makes a statement—a dramatic one. Buy your black lashes with the idea of trimming them to your own look. With nail scissors start clipping the hairs to shape the extra lashes. There are two shapes that are particularly good for Asian eyes. Both are illustrated here. The curved shape with the longest lashes in the center is very good (Figure 23). For younger women who want a spiky look, the eyelashes in Figure 24 work well. Notice that the long ends are noticeably shorter at each corner of the eye.

Fig. 23.                                    Fig. 24.

Holding the extra lashes with tweezers, apply the glue on the lash base and let dry. Apply a narrow line of glue above your own lashes at their base. Add a narrow line of glue to the base of the extra lashes, and apply them to your eye just over your natural lashes, easing them down to the very edge of your lashes. Let them dry. Brush the lashes together, yours and the extra ones.

Evening is a time for fantasy. When you have curled your lashes, or applied extra lashes, consider using blue or purple mascara, an extra touch of color. To bring attention to your eyes, to frame them in light, brush an ivory highlighter across below the eye, and continue it up and out to the temples, brushing it in for softness. Use a light hand for this.

The effects of eyelining, shadowing, and highlighting should be to frame your eyes in light, and to accent and mold your eyes with color—all to emphasize the brilliance of your eyes, your important plus point. Using the techniques that are explained here takes practice, but the results are really worth the effort.

*Evaluate*: Judge for yourself which of the steps we suggest are really the best for your own eyes. And check through the beauty profiles for the kind of creative eye coloring that our role models use.

*Note*: If you wear contact lenses, insert them before making up and remove them before cleansing your face. For the adventuresome, try orange-colored lenses. They will make dark brown Asian eyes look lighter, an interesting switch!

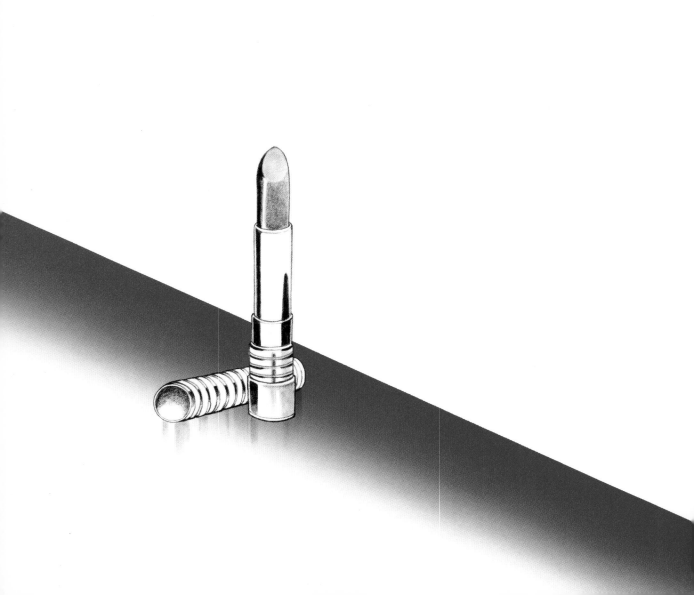

# 10 YOUR MOUTH
## *Defining with Color*

In Chapter 8 you learned how to contour your face to bring out your best points. In Chapter 9 you learned how to shape and emphasize your eye coloring. Now it's time to consider your mouth.

Professionals use a lip brush to shape the mouth. Mastering the technique of brushing lipstick onto the edges of the lips takes time. Lip pencils are a simpler alternative.

Match the shade of your lip pencil as closely as possible to the shade of lipstick that you will wear. "Having your lip pencil a darker shade than the lipstick can make the mouth look hard," says makeup artist Arthur Scott.

Keep in mind that almost everyone uses at least two different colors of lipstick, and many women use two shades at one time, depending on their mood or the color of their clothes. Include at least two colors of lip pencils in your makeup kit.

Your lips should have a base of foundation and be set with powder. Use lip pencil to trace the outline of your lips (Figure 1). This will give you a good edge to follow when applying lipstick, and it will also keep the lipstick from leaking out and smearing.

Remember to follow into the corners of the lips with the pencil. Make a smile line, bringing the lower lipline slightly up at the corners of the mouth. Not too much. Just slightly!

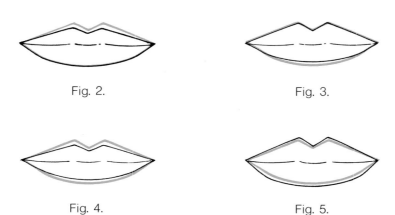

Fig. 1.

Fig. 2.

Fig. 3.

Fig. 4.

Fig. 5.

*Elizabeth Arden* has a *Lip-Fix* that keeps the penciled-in lines in place. It should be applied *before* the moisturizer or foundation. However, putting foundation (powdered, to set it in place) on the lips has somewhat the same effect.

Assess your lip size. If you have a small mouth, or thin lips, you can wear brighter colors—the scarlets, for instance, or coral, or a bright pink. Stay away from red wine shades; they do make the mouth smaller.

If your lips are too full, try the natural tones that look brown in the lipstick tube, and also the red wine shade mentioned before. Wear a red that has a shade of blue in it, instead of a pink that will look light and bright.

If you would like to modify the shape of your lips, visualize the outline of your lips as you would like it to be. Then take the pencil line slightly outside (on the outer edge) of the natural lipline to give fuller lips (Figures 2, 3, 4), or use the pencil slightly inside the lipline for thinner lips (Figure 5). If your lips have uneven curves, this is the chance to make the curves even, with the pencil line. Don't get too far away from the natural contour, the natural edge, of the lip—make the changes very slight.

Often the lipstick color that a person wears is more of a personal choice than a choice of color based on what her makeup should be. Don't let yourself get locked in to wearing one lipstick color every day. It's convenient, but not smart. Your lipstick color should be influenced by the eye coloring you have just now finished in Chapter 9. Or by the colors in your clothes, or earrings, or head scarf—whatever is near your face. Picking up the colors of your outfit increases the impact.

There are certain guidelines. And also a variety of opinions concerning what is best for the Asian face.

Kimi Oshiro at Shiseido uses darker lipstick colors for Asians. She says that Asian lips are thicker. The deeper colors have a thinning effect on the mouth. "There should be contrast on the lips. Use two colors of lipstick," Oshiro advises, "darker on the outside and lighter in the middle." Arthur Scott agrees that this gives the mouth a sexy look. "It gives lips more bounce," he says.

On the other hand, because Asian eyes stand out in the face, and because the eyes are meant to be a focal point, some makeup experts say that paler lipsticks should be used. The color intensity should not be so strong as to direct attention away from the eyes. They suggest a clear, light red, or a deeper cranberry, or a soft coral. "Stay away from pinks," says Scott, while another expert says that a bright pink can be very flattering if the Asian skin has a darker tone. "Pale skins can wear a purple-brown shade and look sophisticated," says Beulah Quo, the Chinese-American actress whose beauty profile appears later in this book. Oshiro, as noted before, says that darker shades should be used because Asian lips are fuller.

Keep in mind that if your skin tone is light, you can wear the deeper shades, like the purple-brown that Beulah Quo says looks sophisticated. If your skin tone is darker, stay with the paler colors—a pink, a coral. What you are looking for is contrast—light skin, darker lipstick; dark skin, lighter lipstick.

Balance the different factors—your skin tone, your mouth size. Experiment. Everyone should have a lipstick with pink or blue-red tones in it, and a lipstick with coral or clear red-wine tones. These are the two basic color divisions in lipsticks, blushers, and nail polish. That's why everyone needs at least two shades of lip pencils, to go with the lipstick colors.

When you use two colors of lipstick together, the darker shade goes over the outside edges and most of the lip area; the lighter

shade goes in the middle of the lips. Lip gloss over lipstick gives an added and effective shine. Use it if you have flat lips or normal lips. If your lips are full and heavy, forget the shine. It will weigh down your mouth, and make your lips protrude too much. A word of encouragement! Lip penciling takes care of almost all size problems. You will probably find that you can wear most of the lipstick shades easily.

*Evening lips.* Artificial lights change colors. Restaurant lighting is usually true, the kind of lighting that you have used when you made up your face. Club or disco lighting changes the colors of your lipstick—and the colors of your eye makeup if you are using pink. Pink fades under fluorescent lighting, and the very dark shades lose their brilliance. Bright pinks, and the deeper plum shades, and wines, should have lip gloss over them, to keep a lively color when you are going out in the evening.

Lipstick colors for image? Pink, coral, and the rusty shades look natural. Scarlet, plum, wine red, and purple look sophisticated. Two-tone lipstick gives a sexy mouth.

Experiment!

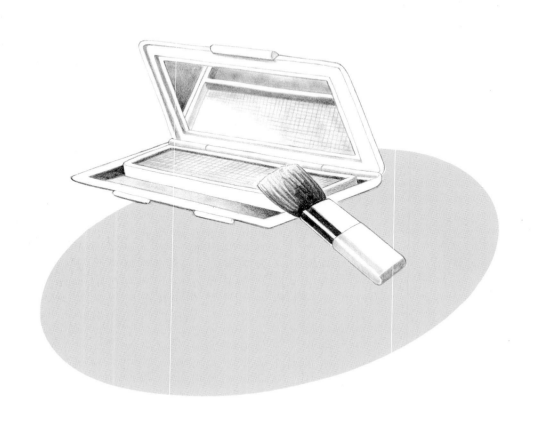

# 11 YOUR CHEEKS
## *Enhancing with Color*

As mentioned earlier, Asian faces have flat surface planes. Contouring these surfaces to create ups and downs, and lows and highs, adds visual interest to your face. Women of other racial backgrounds can use their blusher for contouring, since a blusher will emphasize highs and lows. But it will not create them. Almost all of the face-styling advice on how to use a blusher on different facial shapes does not provide the kind of contouring Asian faces need. You have already accomplished your particular and individual contouring working through Chapter 8.

What Asians need a blusher for is to give a healthy or radiant glow. If you are a blusher addict—and many women are—find a blusher shade that will contour for you, a brown-beige powder blusher, for example, and use it for the contouring techniques. Save the apricot, or peach, or rose shades for the blush of health, a radiant glow. Or to pick up a tired face.

The part of the face that is the highest point of your face is where the color should appear—across the cheekbones toward the ear, a bit on the ear lobe, a dusting on the tip of the chin, and on the forehead. The Asian women whose beauty techniques are in this book speak of a light-toned sparkly powder, a highlighter on the cheekbone—other ways of creating a bright look.

The blushers that professionals recommend for women with Asian features are a peach or apricot or rose shade almost translucent in weight. No one should be aware of color added to the cheeks. Any blush should look like a supremely natural glow.

Both professionals and the women who share their beauty routines in this book stress that very little blusher is necessary. "I just use a little bit over the highest part of my cheeks," says Beulah Quo. Mariko Yandell uses a translucent blusher over the cheekbones and up in a curve to the temples. Kai Yin Lo uses a blusher on the cheekbones, and a bit on the forehead, and the chin. "Occasionally, when I'm tired and traveling, a little bit all over the face to give me a lift," says Kai Yin.

Arthur Scott warns that older women need less blusher than they think. "As women get older, their faces become more angular. There is a natural cheek hollow. It is better to make the cheekbone look rounded, to round and soften the face. I use the blusher right on the outside tip of the cheekbone, put it on the horizontal, and blend it in."

*Note to those in their middle teens*: Don't use a blusher. Your cheeks will gain color as you walk or exercise, or talk or dance. Putting on blusher first, and then gaining natural color can result in fiery red cheeks.

# 12 YOUR EYEBROWS
## *The Face Framers*

Eyebrows are probably the one feature of the face that women pay little attention to, in the way of care. But they are probably one of the most important features of the face in expressing character.

Eyebrows shape the face. Rounded eyebrows look sincere. Eyebrows that go across and then up at the end look sharp on thin faces, but balance a heavy jaw with others. A natural arch looks most sophisticated.

"Women with Asian features need strong eyebrows, rather thick, to balance the eye area," says Kimi Oshiro.

The eyebrow should start slightly toward the middle of the face from the inner eye corner. Pluck hairs that grow between the brows above the bridge of the nose.

Since it is highly unnatural to have brows that grow in a neat line, don't pluck your eyebrow hairs to form a rigid line. Take out the strays, but allow a bit of unevenness along the line of the brow.

Now it's time to evaluate, before shaping. Using a sharpened brown eyeliner pencil, or *Clinque's Brow Shaper*, draw tiny lines, the thinness of one hair, to try out different shapes.

If your face is round, shape a gentle curve that has the outside end of the brow continuing in a straight line, or slightly up. If your face is square, try a shape that goes into a down curve at the outer end. With

a rectangular face, try the look of a straight-across eyebrow. The triangular face gets a gentle curve. Don't exaggerate the shape. Evaluate.

When you have decided what browline you like, pluck gently to coax out that shape. Think twice before plucking above the browline. Don't let the eyebrow get narrow, except at the outer end where it narrows naturally. The eyebrow should arch just outside the center of the eye, and end at a point above, or slightly beyond, the outer corner of the eye. Look in a three-way mirror. Check that your eyebrow does not grow so far across that it is too near the hairline at the temple, seen in profile. That is likely to be the narrowest part of the Asian face, which is why the eyebrow should not extend much beyond the outer corner of the eye.

For the part of eyebrows where hair is stiff, and grows in the wrong direction, use a bit of hairspray on an eyebrow brush and then brush the hairs into shape.

Remember to always brush your eyebrows after using powder. Keep them neat and dark, an accent for your eyes.

# 13 YOUR HAIR
## *Styling, Coloring, and Care*

Remember that being a brunette is a plus factor. The contrast of dark hair against your skin provides a vivid frame for your face that can make your look—whatever you want it to be—even more striking.

Your glossy, black hair, with its volume, is a tremendous asset. Keeping it in good condition provides you with that strong plus factor.

Two international hairstylists with thorough knowledge of both Asian and non-Asian hair have contributed their professional opinions which we share with you in this section.

International hairstylist Suga is based in New York and creates styles for fashion ads, *Vogue* photos, and professional personalities like actress/model Brooke Shields, skater Dorothy Hamill, and a long list of others. He also directs and creates styles for his seven salons in Japan. Japanese hairstylist Fumio Kawashima creates trend-setting styles in his three Peek-a-Boo salons in Tokyo, and does styling demonstrations in Hong Kong, Taiwan, and Singapore. He was formerly a creative director for Vidal Sassoon in London.

## STYLING ASIAN HAIR

Suga says that Asian hair feels coarser in the hand, and looks as if it has more volume, and that both of these factors are important in selecting a hairstyle.

"You should think about the fact that Asian heads are often flat at the back of the crown of the head," Suga says. "There should be more volume in that area." With a short cut, the volume can be achieved by using rollers at the back of the crown, or blow drying the hair with a roller brush that coaxes up more volume in that area. Brush the hair up, and from each side to the back, to keep hair on that part of the head from flattening out. With longer hair (neither stylist recommends hair longer than shoulder length) the same brushing, with more brushing up over the top of the head from the back, should work. If not, rollers can be used in that area when drying your hair.

Suga warns, however, "Too much volume isn't good. Dark hair looks heavy, and if it's thick it will look heavier." To prevent a top-heavy look of thick, dark hair, Suga stresses that you need a good haircut that will shape your hair and emphasize its glossy quality.

It is also necessary to have a styling that is slightly closer to the head than with non-Asian hair.

"Asian heads look larger in proportion to their bodies," Suga continues. "Women should look at themselves in a full-length mirror, to find the right proportion of volume for their size. It's necessary to balance the height, and the head. Too much volume gives a heavy-headed look." Most women consider the shape of their face when deciding on a new hairstyle, but Suga maintains that Asian women should consider their body proportions before going on to the face shape and a new styling.

When it comes to cutting, there are two methods: a blunt cut, and a tapered cut. This has nothing to do with the final styling. It's a technique. In a blunt cut, the ends are cut straight across, even when the lengths are different. In a tapered cut, the ends are cut irregularly. Suga says, "The best cut for Asian hair is a blunt cut. It is the easiest to maintain, it looks better, and it shines more. With some Asian hair, the quality of the hair around the ears and the nape of the neck is different. That part of the cut might have to be tapered, but the general cut should be blunt."

Fumio Kawashima agrees: "A blunt cut is the only kind that works well for Asian hair. It emphasizes the sheen of the hair, and the texture looks good." He continues, "Chinese and Korean women have thinner hair than Japanese do. They like a layered cut at the back."

Kawashima adds a warning about the strength of Asian hair. "Asian hair breaks easily. People think it's stronger, but it's not. With coarse hair, you have to be careful. Also, Asian hair has more split ends." He, too, mentions the fact that the back of the head is flat, and requires volume.

Both Suga and Kawashima are reluctant to discuss actual styles. Hairstyles come and go, but the way the hair is treated, the kind of cut it requires, the amount of volume it needs, and the kind of care that should be taken, does not change.

Suga points out that many Asians have faces that narrow in at the temples, and this fact should be considered in styling. Covering that part of the hairline with softness of some kind conceals the hairline, and may give a better shape to the face.

Kawashima says that the face shape is not as important as the allover proportions. "I look at the woman standing up, her height, and her head in relation to her body. Then it's more a matter of her personality and the kind of clothes she likes to wear. I like a one-length cut, because Asian hair hangs well, and has texture and sheen. You can change the front, have maybe a little fringe around one part of the face. But the one-length cut, that reaches to the chin, is very good. You can wear it pushed back if you want."

What to do with curly or wavy hair? Kawashima says, "Have it

straightened. There's a new process that doesn't damage the hair. It's a protein treatment. It takes time, a couple of hours. But the hair comes out very straight and shiny, and the texture is improved."

For women who want a different cut, and are not happy with straight hair—no matter how glossy it is and how well it swings into shape—there are alternatives.

One is to have the blunt cut—which, remember, is the cutting technique, not the result!—and then to have the edges fringed around the face, tapered toward the face during cutting. This hair-style is easy to arrange—with a permanent—into a natural styling that allows softness over the forehead. Or it can be set into little wisps, a waving, or tendrils, over the temples. Or it can be combed back to frame, the face with the edges going back and up. There are endless variations to this face-framing cutting style.

"Remember, Asian hair should be bent. It shouldn't be curled," Kawashima says.

Another creative facestylist lists nine face types, by personality rather than face shape. Seven out of the nine have straight hair.

Whether you decide to have straight, wavy or curly hair is up to you yourself, but remember to look in a full-length mirror, and try to visualize yourself with the new styling, to see if it is right for your proportions.

## PERMANENTS

"Permanents are easy to do on Asian hair. It takes less time for the process. A weaker solution should be used. The pH point is lower," Kawashima says.

## HAIR COLORING

Hair stylists are violenty opposed to drastic changes of hair color for Asians. It doesn't agree with the skin coloring, and it kills the texture and shine. Both Suga and Kawashima point out that Asian women should not change the color of their hair more than two shades lighter, or two shades darker, than their natural hair. "Some women think that a lighter hair color is more softening to the face," Suga says, "but the maximum lightening should only be two shades lighter. This will give good highlights."

"The most effective, and the best choice in coloring, is the semi-permanent rinse," Suga said. "It does the least damage to the hair. The color coats the hair shaft; it does not penetrate it. The effect lasts from four to six weeks."

## GRAY HAIR

Suga suggests coating gray hair until it becomes about 50% gray all over the head. "After that, it looks good as it is," he noted.

The semi-permanent rinse, just mentioned as doing the least damage to the hair, is effective in coating the gray. Use a tone that is two shades lighter than the original color of your hair. Brown henna will also coat the gray in hair. It serves as a hair conditioner as well. If you are using a semi-permanent hair coloring at home, Suga suggests using the foam type. Keep it on for double the amount of time suggested, in order to coat the gray. "It's safe," he says.

A home rinse for darkening hair, and coating gray, involves the use of sage leaves. Pour boiling water over two to three ounces of sage leaves, or steep the leaves in one pint of tea. Another recipe is to pour boiling water over crushed cloves or walnuts. Let it cool naturally. Apply either one as a final rinse.

Have a permanent *before* getting your hair colored, not after. Wait for three days after the permanent before having hair colored with a semi-permanent rinse. Wait one week if you are having a permanent color change.

## TEMPORARY COLORS . . . FOR FUN

Haircolor sprays, to add bright or pale color to the hair, are fun to use, and will not damage hair. The color washes out with shampooing.

Kawashima says that the paler colors—bright white, bright yellow, and pale blue—on part, not all, of your hair are "great for a party look."

## SHAMPOOS

Although Asian hair is different in texture and volume from non-Asian hair (see Chapter 4), much of the care and treatment is the same.

Hair should be washed every day in the summer, and probably two to five times a week in the winter. Conditioners, sprays, and mousses, plus dirt and perspiration make this necessary for clean, healthy hair.

Dirty hair carries negative ions, and to clean it you have to reverse the charge, make it alkaline. Adult shampoos are alkaline. Baby shampoos, which are not alkaline (to avoid irritating babies' eyes) do not clean adult hair efficiently.

What kind of shampoo should you use? Many shampoos are labelled according to type of hair: dry, normal, or oily hair. Use what seems right for your hair. If it appears to make the hair dull, switch to another which is labelled for tinted or damaged hair. These are often the gentlest in cleansing action.

Oily hair should be washed daily. Give it one good soaping each time, and a thorough rinsing. An old-time recipe for treating oily hair is to work baking soda into the clean, wet hair, to absorb excess oil, and then rinse thoroughly. It leaves the hair shiny.

Normal hair, and dry hair, not washed quite as often, should have two soapings and thorough rinsings. Rinse for two or three minutes,

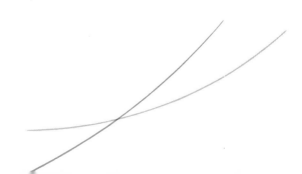

longer than you think is necessary. Suga suggests ending with a cold-water rinse, which closes the pores of the scalp, and sometimes gives added glossiness.

## RINSES AND CONDITIONERS

Because Asian hair tends to split, rinses seem important. Both Suga and Kawashima say that having your hair trimmed once a month is the best way to deal with split ends.

Normal hair does not need a creamy rinse after shampooing. A rinse is needed only to untangle hair that is difficult to comb.

Oily hair needs an acid rinse for more shine. For oily hair, Suga suggests a homemade rinse of one pint of water to the juice of half a lemon, or a pint of wate rand one cup of vinegar. The vinegar smell will disappear with the dampness.

Conditioning rinses come in two types. The instant conditioner coats the hair shaft, and the effect lasts until the next shampoo. Penetrating conditioners, left on for twenty minutes or longer, add nutrients to the hair shaft. These conditioners must be rinsed or washed out. Check the instructions.

Suga says that people with normal hair don't need conditioners, or should use only instant conditioners. Those with oily hair should use the rinse suggested above. Those with dry hair should use an instant conditioner at every shampoo, and a penetrating conditioner once every ten days.

While sunbathing, he suggests that you comb conditioner through the hair, and tie your hair back. Wash it thoroughly afterwards. The sun has a strong drying effect, and the conditioner will counteract this.

Clean, shining, healthy hair is a wonderful asset. You have the glossiness, and the fullness. Treat it well!

# 14 THE MATURE WOMAN
## *Your Special Needs*

Let's assume that you've read the chapter about face treatment, and the differences between Asians and non-Asians, and the other material that is presented in this book.

There are a few things that apply particularly to older women, and that are absolutely necessary for your skin care.

Eye cream, for one. It should be applied both at night, and in the morning under your daytime makeup. It is a fact that younger women are more careful about using eye cream than their mothers are. Eye cream is a relatively new product, and women have a tendency to continue doing what was a habit when they were young. If you haven't used eye cream before, you may not realize what an important part of skin treatment eye creams can be. Eye cream will smooth out lines, little wrinkles and folds, and give a more youthful appearance. It is a necessity for your skin care, and will make a noticeable difference in your appearance.

Another product that you should use is an eyeshadow foundation. *Elizabeth Arden's Eye-Fix* is a particularly good for you since it is colorless, and you will be contouring your eyes in a totally different way from non-Asian women. An eyeshadow foundation also works to smooth out the tiny lid wrinkles, and provides a base that will keep your eyeshadow from fading, messing, or cracking.

One of the problem areas for older women is their mouth, and the tiny lines around it. *Elizabeth Arden* has *Lip-Fix,* to keep your lipstick from smearing over and entering the tiny lines that surround the mouth. This cream also plumps out those little lines, and should be considered a necessity in a more mature woman's cosmetic kit. Apply and then let dry, and then use a lip pencil to define the shape of your mouth. Apply lipstick over this, using the lip pencil edging as a guide, and filling in the lips with color.

Older skin is more fragile, and more dry. You must be particularly careful about going out in the sun without adequate sun protection. Re-read the section about sun prevention lotions and foundations with a sunscreen. Older skin has a tendency to develop brown spots quickly after exposure to the sun. Protect your skin!

You need a good moisturizer to wear under your makeup, and over your night cream, if you are using a skin-renewal preparation. If you are not using a skin-renewal preparation, you really should try it.

Feeding your skin is twice as important as it was when you were younger! If your skin is healthy and well-fed, if you have the right foundation for your makeup, you're already jumped a number of the hurdles that proclaim your age.

This is the time to be most vigilant about the little things. It is the time when you must have a magnifying mirror to check your skin condition, and to help you when you apply your makeup. It is the time to remember to use skin tonic in the morning as well as at night, to keep your pores closed and smooth. It is the time to pat your face gently with the middle and fourth finger—patting up and out lightly. Do this for the area beside the mouth, on each side—and the area of the cheeks that reach to the nose.

This is the time to do all the little things that you remember from the past but have become lazy about doing! Remember to have an efficient facial treatment routine every night and every morning. After two weeks you'll see the difference that these little things do in making a smoother, healthier face!

You need a face mask at least once a week. Women have known for ages that a beaten-up egg white is a great face-smoother. Leave it on till it dries, then wash off with cold water. It's more effective than anything in a tube or jar for smoothing and tightening facial skin.

If the egg-white mask is drying for your skin, use the recipe in Chapter 6—one tablespoon of honey and half an egg white beaten together, then folded into a beaten egg yolk. This nourishes, softens, and smooths out the facial skin. Apply it to a clean, dry face (having first put eye cream all around the eye socket over the lid). Wash it off with cool water as soon as it starts to get dry. There are also purifying masks that deep-cleanse the skin, and gentle face scrubs that should be used according to directions. This means that you should scrub gently, then rinse gently several times.

There is one other thing. Older women lose porosity in their bones; the bones become more brittle. There are estrogen preparations that prevent this, but many doctors disapprove of them. The alternative is to take a calcium preparation each day, to prevent bone brittleness. *Os-Cal* is one such preparation.

Now that you have treated your face well—feeding it, smoothing it, and preparing it for subtle makeup—let's go on to your hair and cosmetics.

If your hair is becoming gray—whether you cover the gray or not—your skin tone is also probably changing. The colors that you found so attractive when younger may not work well for you now. This is not just because of your hair; it is because your skin tone changes when your hair color changes.

It's important to keep an open mind about makeup, and to

change your makeup colors, to experiment with what is right for you now. Almost everyone is reluctant to give up makeup techniques that worked well in the past, but you have changed, and so have your makeup needs.

It is an absolute fact that older women cannot wear strong colors on their faces. Or glittery shadows or lipsticks. Strong colors, and shiny-surfaced makeup are cruel to mature faces with little wrinkles and lines.

Most women "of a certain age," as the French so nicely put it, find that coral is a supremely natural and pleasing color, both in lipsticks and in blushers. The blushers can be paler, showing just a touch of color.

There should be less contouring than recommended in Chapter 8. The face exhibits more bone structure as it ages. "Don't contour your cheeks," says makeup artist Arthur Scott, "the look is too harsh. Use just a bit of blusher, over the cheekbone and straight out to the hairline."

If your jawline sags at each side, contour gently over that area. Do use a contour powder or darker base under the jaw, where a double chin may start. And consider using some at each side of the neck, where the strong tendons below each ear may stand out. And cover your eyelid with the darker shade of contouring powder or darker foundation.

Older women may have plucked their brows too thin in the past, with the hair not growing back to give the eyebrows definition. If your brows are thin, take the gray eyeliner pencil, sharpen it, and draw tiny lines, hair-thin lines to shape and fill in the brow. Don't let the end of the eyebrow turn down. A crescent that goes straight across, rounding up about one-third of the distance from the inner eye, is a good shape for you.

About your eyes. A brown or medium gray eyeliner pencil is best for you. Black eyeliner is not flattering.

Study your eyes in the magnifying mirror. Older eyes tend to droop at the corners. If you have a tiny fold above the lashline, use a light blue or green eyeliner tracing there.

If your lids have a tendency to droop at each corner, be sure that your brown or gray eyeliner pencil covers this droop.

When makeup people talk about soft colors for older women, they mean lighter colors. Never choose a color that is darker than a medium shade. Teal blue—a medium blue-green—is exceptionally pretty as a shadowing above the lid. Use it at each outside third of the eyeball; leave the middle lighter. Blend it well, out and up slightly. You can even go paler in color—experiment using a soft green or lavender, putting a little light brown over it, if you think the color is too definite. You'll find that as you get used to the pale color, you won't need the brown overlay.

Evaluate your beauty routine. Use your creams daily, and the egg mask at least once a week, and notice the difference!

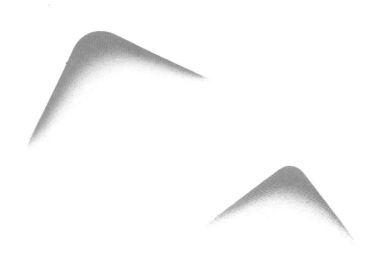

# 15 FRAGRANCE
## *For Individuality*

The finishing touch to a makeup and hairstyling session is the decision upon a fragrance—the perfume, or eau de toilette or cologne that will best project your individuality, the one that suits you best.

What makes a scent individual is the way it reacts to your body chemistry. There is no "Asian body chemistry" as such. People have different ideas in labelling perfumes, as is obvious in what is called an Oriental scent. It is usually heavy, but no more appropriate to Asians than any other scent would be.

Choosing a scent involves do's and don'ts. Don't buy it without trying it on your skin first. Allow a perfume at least twenty minutes to develop on your skin, and then decide if you like it. Perfumes have a top note, a middle note and a base fragrance. The top note is what you smell in the bottle, and immediately after applying it. The middle note and base notes are what you smell on your skin after twenty minutes of wearing it, and what clings to your clothes for days after a wearing.

Don't choose a scent because it smells delicious on a friend. People have different body chemistries, and perfumes react differently, smell different, on different skins.

What smells wonderful in the winter may be too heavy a fragrance in warm weather. What smells wonderfully fresh in the summer can

be too light in cold weather. When the season changes, readjust your perfume thinking.

Most people think of an eau de toilette for daytime use, a perfume for evening wear. What's the difference?

Perfume is the extract, the strongest scent, and lasts longer on the skin, from two to six hours. Eau de toilette is the same scent diluted with water, and can last from two to four hours on the skin, as a lighter version of the perfume. Eau de cologne is the lightest, lasting about one hour. Cologne is refreshing for summer wear, or for casual daytime use. All scents should be renewed after four hours.

Categories like sexy, sophisticated, or sporty may be of use in deciding what to try on your skin. However, once you've found a scent you like, ask what's in it. It may be grouped as a citrus (bergamot) scent, or a light combination of florals, or a rose fragrance, or a jasmine and spice mixture. These are the predominant top and middle notes of a fragrance. If you particularly like one kind, other fragrances that fit into that group will also be interesting to you.

Once you've bought a fragrance, take care that it lasts as long as you want it to. Replace the top firmly after using it, since scents evaporate. Store perfumes and eau de toilettes in a dry, dark place, since they lose qualities, deteriorate, in the light. Don't pour it into a plastic bottle for travel or convenience in carrying around. The plastic changes the composition of the fragrance.

Where do you apply it to the skin? At the pulse points, where the skin is warmest—inside the elbows, wrists, knees and ankles, and under the breasts, and behind the ears. Don't apply it on the neck and down the cleavage; you will smell it too strongly. Your nose will get used to it, and refuse to notice it after a week, or month.

As an addition to that point, remember that even if you get used to it, and don't notice it on your skin, it remains just as noticeable to others. Don't increase the amount you use!

One particular plus point in collecting perfumes, and using them, is that the empty bottles still carry the fragrance, and are wonderful to tuck into a drawer to scent underwear or scarves. Or to display— some perfume bottles are magnificent designs, highly collectible!

## Some Final Words

Have a good, interesting time experimenting with these techniques for care, and styling, and color.

Use restraint. If you look all color and contour, you're not transmitting the styling message. It should be subtle.

Have confidence!

You look great!

# THE PROFILES

JAE EUN CHOI

ALENE DE LA HOUSSAYE

NORA AKINO

MADELEINE KIM

KAI YIN LO

RAMONA AUYONG

BEULAH QUO

CARRIE YAMAOKA

MARIKO YANDELL

TERESA MA

CAROLE KAI

## JAE EUN CHOI

*Jae Eun Choi is Korean. She is an artist, ceramist, and flower arrangement teacher. She is a valued associate of Headmaster Teshigahara of the Sōgetsu School of Japanese flower arrangement. Born in Seoul, Jae Eun now lives in Japan, in between business trips to Europe and the Asian continent for a flower wholesaler. Jae Eun has an authoritative boldness of concept. Her stunning arrangements—a recent arrangement was a sculptural interpretation of dark, damp earth, contoured, and containing sweeping islands of tiny new grass shoots—have garnered her an appreciative group of admirers. Jae Eun is writing a book on art, interweaving the themes of ceramics, arrangements, and found objects.*

### JAE EUN'S MAKEUP

"I have dry skin in winter, and use *Carita's Cream Makeup.* In the summer I use *Shiseido's Water-Based Foundation.* I try to match my skin color when selecting products."

"I use blue and brown pencils for my eyebrows in the summer, drawing little hairs. In the winter I use brown."

"For my eyes I use a dark brown eye pencil. Then above the eye I put a gray/blue mix, and then over that, and up to the brow, an orange/gold mix. I take this out beyond the brow line, toward the temple. These are powder eyeshadows."

"I use highlights. My face changes shape when I gain or lose weight. I use a powder highlighter, dark ivory, and go around the chin and up to the ear on each side. Then I put it on the cheekbones, and under the eye and up around to the temples."

"In the evening, I use an almost white cream base under the eyes."

"I wear my hair slicked back. I work hard, and it gets in the way."

"At night I wash my face, then use skin lotion, then night cream and eye cream."

"I use translucent powder all over the face."

"I don't do this all the time, only when I'm going out. I don't use much makeup when I'm working."

## ALENE DE LA HOUSSAYE

*Alene de la Houssaye is a Japanese-American married to Abe de la Houssaye. They are a chef-manager team of the two trendy New York restaurants they own, La Louisiana, and Texarkana. Before her marriage, Alene studied at San Jose State and the University of Oregon, and then had her own accessories design business in New York. She has two daughters, Susannah and Aimee, both under two years of age. Alene's complexion is very fair, and her choice of makeup colors is influenced by this.*

### ALENE'S MAKEUP

"I do what's easiest. I just accentuate what's there."

"When I was pregnant, my skin got dry, so I went to *Ronald Sherman*. He's a dermatologist. I use his products—his cleanser and cream."

"I use a light moisturizer in the summer, and a heavier one in the winter."

"For a foundation, I use *Clinique's Balanced Makeup* in their lightest shade. In the winter, I use their *Extra Help Makeup*, with water. I put it on my neck, and lips, too."

"Then I apply *Maybelline Light Concealer* under my eyes, and on the far side of each eyebrow."

"Next, I take *Clinique's Gray Eyeshadow* and use it wet, with a brush, and line my eyes, all the way out."

"Then I take an intense color, like *Borghese's Eyeshadow Mousse*, a cream that is dark purple and a bit sparkly. I put it on with my finger, above the lashline from the center going up and out. I take it beyond the eye corner, then blend it from the middle of the eye socket up and out, so that it's lighter at the edges. Under the brow I use sparkly ivory powder."

"Then I use an eyelash curler, and *Maybelline Mascara*, black. Make sure the top ones are dry before doing the bottom ones! I wear contact lenses, by the way."

"My eyebrow hairs grow down, so I comb them up."

"I apply *Elizabeth Arden Lip-Fix* with my little finger, and let it dry, and then use a brush to apply lipstick. I use clear red or cranberry lipsticks, real matte. I don't like them shiny. And a pale blusher, almost no blush."

"I put on *Lancome's Powder*, freely, then pat my face with a towel to take off the excess."

"I don't brush my hair. I wash it, and blow-dry it, and then use *Tenax* or a mousse to hold the hair up and away from the face. I think Japanese have pretty foreheads. Putting the hair back from the face opens the face. I like to see little wisps of hair around the edges, in front of the ears and in back. I think it looks very pretty."

"I wear black, red, white, or pink clothes. I stay away from yellow or green because if I wear these colors, I turn yellow or green."

"Since I work in a low-light atmosphere I use more makeup at night. I intensify the colors. More of the eyeshadow mousse. And blue eyeshadow over the mousse, at each side above the eye, and on the outside below the lower lid. It opens the eyes. I use a kohl pencil under the lashes, and smudge it to make the eyes look very dark. And I use more blusher, and mascara. And then *Clinique's Translucent Luminescent Finishing Powder*. It sparkles."

## NORA AKINO

*Nora Akino was born in Japan. She entered Stanford University as a California State Scholar and graduated with a degree in English. A Phi Beta Kappa, Nora was a member of the university choir and also studied modern dance. She enjoys painting, drawing, backpacking, and white-water rafting. She has spent the past year studying Japanese at the prestigious Inter-University Center for Japanese Language Studies in Tokyo. Nora has a strong interest in the arts and would like to study Japanese painting.*

*Often encouraged to model, Nora has been wearing makeup for only one year and explains, "I liked the natural look, and applying makeup seemed like too much trouble. But I'm reconsidering and gradually experimenting with different techniques. The air in Tokyo is not very clean and I'm very concerned about my skin."*

## NORA'S MAKEUP

"I don't use a foundation. Instead, I use *Lancome's Protective Day Cream*."

"For my eyes, I like a beige-mauve eyeshadow. Shiny. I don't wear blue shadow. That's too much color for me. I like the browns, the violets, and the green shades. I think they look more natural."

"I use *Lancome's Water-Based Mascara*. It has a beeswax base, and is soluble, more organic. I wear contact lenses, so I have to be careful."

"I use brown eyeliner, on the fold of the eye."

"I don't use a blusher or powder. My lipstick is a translucent reddish brown."

"I wash my face with *Clinique Soap*, and use their *Clarifying Lotion*. I use *Lancome's Nutribel* at night."

"The only treatment I do is for my hair. I use henna, mostly red with black, and apply it to a whole strand, and leave it on for a couple of hours. I coat each strand."

## MADELEINE KIM

*Of Korean heritage, Madeleine Kim grew up in Shanghai, then went to Germany and Austria to study, and now lives in Japan. She is a former visiting lecturer in philosophy at the University of Tokyo, and is now involved in the formation of the International Center for Comparative Philosophy and Aesthetics, as well as lecturing on contemporary philosophy at the new University of the Air (broadcasting) in Tokyo. Madeleine is fluent in Korean, Japanese, German, and English, "with some Chinese," and is married to economist, ceramist, and ceramics collector B.C. Rhee.*

## MADELEINE'S MAKEUP

"I don't do very much to my face."

"For foundation, I use a creamy emulsion, and match it to my skin color. In the summertime, I use a little stronger color."

"For eyeshadow, I use a purple/brown base all over the eye socket, blending it in, then a little blue/green over it on the outside. I use black eyeliner, and black mascara on my lashes, in the evening."

"Both my lipstick and my blusher are very pale, the blusher a peach/pink, and the lipstick a peach shade. At night it's a little darker, more pink."

"I don't use powder."

"I wash my face with a soapless soap that I get in Austria, then use a tonic without alcohol, and *Lancome's Night Cream*. Under my makeup I use *Hydrex*, a moisturizer. And an eye cream, at night and in the morning."

## KAI YIN LO

*Kai Yin Lo is a highly successful jewelry and accessories designer whose designs are featured in leading stores in the United States—Saks Fifth Avenue and Neiman Marcus—and in London at Harrods and Harvey Nichols, as well as her boutiques in Tokyo and her native Hong Kong. Kai Yin also designs for the Paris and Tokyo fashion collections of Hanae Mori and other world-famous designers. Kai Yin says that her unique jewelry is for working women, and women who travel. Her private clients include a roster of well-known names, such as Queen Noor of Jordan and Mrs. William Randolph Hearst, Jr.*

*Kai Yin studied history at Cambridge University and the University of London. She worked with Time, Inc. in New York and did flower arrangements for Constance Spry before beginning her design work.*

*How do you recognize Kai Yin Lo designs? Her jewelry can be worn with sports and dress clothes. It is a soft mixture of colors and materials—hematite and pearls and ivory and antique ceramics, for instance—in a sensible, fashionable melange. Snoopy fans may remember Kai Yin for the outfits that she designed for the Snoopy and Belle doll exhibition that traveled across the U.S. and then went on to Europe and Japan.*

### KAI YIN'S MAKEUP

"I believe in simplicity, partly because I'm traveling most of the time. I keep makeup in my New York apartment, and in Hong Kong at home, and in the office, and I have makeup in my bag all the time, along with a bit of cream. This way I can makeup in the car if I have to."

"I use different cosmetic colors when I'm in New York and when I'm in Hong Kong. It depends on the weather, and the clothes I'm wearing."

"With foundation, I try to match the skin of my face. In winter, I use a light cream base of *Borghese's*, and in the summer a water-based *Lancome* foundation. When I'm tanned I use nothing."

"I use a silver-pink moisturizer, *Chanel Cream Rouge*, as an eyeshadow base and as a highlight. I put it on my forehead, too, and under my eyes."

"I line the bottom lashline with midnight blue, and the top with brown liner. I have double-fold eyelids, and I put midnight blue liner there, across the top from about the middle to the outer corner. It gives emphasis. I add a dark plummy red over the lid toward the end of the eye. Under the brow, I use a darker pink for evening. And I also use mascara at night."

"For lipstick I use a pink shade, I like it better than orange. At night, I use a darker pink, and add a little lip gloss over. It makes a difference."

"My blusher is dark pink. I use it over the cheekbone, quite close to the under-eye area. I believe in using blusher. I think it's important. Sometimes I put it all over my face, for a lift."

"I use the darkest shade of powder."

"I use a light night cream in the summer, *Lancaster*, and a heavier one in the winter. Most of my creams are *Lancome* or *Borghese* or *La Prairie*. I switch products. I think the skin needs the change, the stimulation, of something new."

"Really the best thing to do for your skin is to get enough sleep. My skin just glows, taking off three or four years, when I have time to sleep."

"I use *Evian Water* when I fly because the cabin is so dry. I mist it onto my face, and add a bit of cream in cold weather."

"I wash my face in summer, and use an astringent. In winter I wash it every other day, alternating this with a day of cleansing cream, tonic, and cream."

"Twice a week I use a mask, when I'm traveling. In Hong Kong I have someone who comes in to do a facial."

## RAMONA AUYONG

*Ramona Auyong is executive director of the Barbizon Modeling School and Agency in Hawaii. She has a degree in business management from the University of Hawaii, in addition to being a former beauty title holder and model with print work and television commercial credits. Ramona jogs for 3–4 miles at least three times a week and feels that seven to eight hours of sleep every night is essential for good health. She eats a balanced diet but avoids red meat and butter. Ramona is of Chinese and Hawaiian descent.*

### RAMONA'S MAKEUP

"My beauty routine centers on the use of *Barbizon* products, and the things I mention below are all from *Barbizon* unless otherwise stated."

"First I wash my face with *Foam Wash*, and then use an astringent. *Day Moist* is what I use as an under-foundation moisturizer. I use *Clinique's Daily Eye Treat*. Once a week I use *Barbizon Deep Cleanser* for pores, which is a combination of honey, oatmeal, and almond extract. Then a few days later I use *Mint Masque*. I think a good cleanser is essential in the humid Hawaiian climate."

"I use a creamy ivory foundation, and put a lavender color corrector under it to help erase yellow tones. Over the foundation goes a translucent powder, brushed on for a matte finish. I contour my cheeks with blusher, taking it up to the temples to counteract my round cheeks. *Raspberry Frost* is the color I use when I'm wearing blue or pink, and *Bronze* is the shade I use when I'm wearing rust, orange, cream, or brown tones."

"I like to use powder shadow in dark smoky tones—brown, navy, deep plum, and olive green. I line my lower lid with brown."

"Then I use a combination of colors on the top lid, being careful to extend the colors beyond the eye. I end by using a toast color highlighter under the brow. I use *Lancome's Stylucil Mascara*, very lightly. I outline my lips with a pencil in a darker shade than my lipstick, then use a deep pink with the raspberry blusher, or a red-orange with the bronze blusher."

## BEULAH QUO

*A Chinese-American actress, producer, and grandmother, Beulah Quo was a Phi Beta Kappa in sociology at the University of California at Berkeley and received an M.A. from the University of Chicago before starting her acting career. An Emmy nominee for her television work, Beulah was in the Oscar-winning* Chinatown *and has also appeared in the* Hawaii Five-0 *series. Off the screen, Beulah has served as president of The China Society and is currently a board member.*

### BEULAH'S MAKEUP

"I don't wear much makeup when I'm not working. I think a natural look is better."

"I use a moist cream foundation. *Bill Tuttle*, a former Hollywood makeup man, has good colors. I use his beige and medium beige, and mix it, with a touch of rose, to match my skin."

"I use an eyeliner, and then a black art pencil (*Eberhard Faber Extra Smooth,* #65). Over this I blend up from the lashes *Clinique's Mauve Eyeshadow*—from the nose bridge out and across, about halfway up to the eyebrow. No mascara—I wear contact lenses. I pull on my lashes gently, to get the loose ones off, and encourage them to grow."

"I use a cream rouge in winter, to accent my high cheekbones. I mix a mauve/purple shade for evening, or for daytime, an orange/ clove brown mix, for my cheeks, and the same colors for my lips."

"I don't like pink tones. They don't go well with Asian skins."

"My eyebrows have a natural arch. I darken them with the art pencil, one hair at a time. Then I use an eyebrow brush."

"Sometimes I do a dark shadow along the side of the nose, then rub it away. Too much makes you look old."

"For evening, I use a touch of white on the nose bridge, and on the eyebone below the brow, and a bit of gloss over my lipstick. I never use powder."

"I also never wash my face with soap. I use a cleanser, tonic, and *Skin Dew*

*Moisturizer.* Occasionally I splash my face with warm water. Cold water isn't good for the skin."

"I do *tai chi* every day. It increases circulation, and improves muscle tone. It's convenient. I can do it on location."

## CARRIE YAMAOKA

*Carrie Yamaoka is a Japanese-American painter in New York, where home is a loft across the river in Hoboken. Graduated from Wesleyan University in fine arts, Carrie exhibits her work in New York and New Jersey galleries, and is currently working in Saratoga Springs under a foundation grant.*

### CARRIE'S MAKEUP

"I don't do anything very special, and I do the same thing all the time."

"I match my foundation to my skin color. It's water-based, not creamy."

"I don't use powder."

"I use Persian violet shadow all over the eye socket. I blend it in, so that it's lighter on the highest part of the eye, and up above, under the brow."

"Then, on the outer half of the eye socket, I use a teal shadow, shaded over the violet."

"I put a little bit of bright yellow under the brow, and smooth it."

"I use an eyelash curler, and then black mascara."

"I don't use a blusher much, but when I do it's a red-brown."

"I change my lipstick often, use whatever I feel like using. But it's usually a rusty red."

"At night I use more of the same colors. I never use powder."

"I wash my face, and use a skin tonic, and a cream moisturizer at night, and a moisturizing lotion for day. I use *Clinique.*"

"Occasionally I get a spot, and I use a stick concealer for that."

## MARIKO YANDELL

*Mariko Yandell was born in Yokohama to a Japanese mother and an American father. Her family lives in California, where her father is a physician. After graduating from high school, Mariko lived in Paris for two years and studied at the Paris Opera Ballet. She then returned to California and danced as soloist with the Oakland Ballet. Mariko has a B.A. in Asian Studies from the University of California, Berkeley, and is now in Tokyo studying classical Japanese dance.*

### MARIKO'S MAKEUP

"Color charting restricts Asians. We have a wider choice of what we can wear."

"I have fair skin. I can use a lot of color. My eyes have a slight fold, the socket is round, and my lashes are straight. I have oily skin, so I use *Erno Laszlo*'s routine of soap and controlling lotion, and *Shake-It* (an alcohol, talc, and pigment foundation)."

"With the *Shake-It Foundation*, I mix two colors: blush, and light beige. It has a natural matte finish, and provides a very light coverage. I use *Laszlo's Phelitone Concentrate* under my eyes, and *Borghese's Eyeshadow Base*, or *Elizabeth Arden Eye-Fix*."

"I line the underneath lashes with brown. Then I like to use the lightest lip pencil, like a pink, and line the top with that, and then go over it with a strong blue. It comes out a lovely violet. Or I use brown both top and bottom for the lashes, and then *Dior's Eyeshadow Set* with four colors."

"Using the *Brun* shadow I make a V at the outer edge of the eye, going from the lashes to the outer corner, and then back toward the crease. I make it dark, and blend it towards the middle. I use *Rose Tartare* next to it near the middle of the eye, and then *Terra Rosa* from the crease upwards. In the corner near the nose I use *Peche* and also under the brow at the outer corner. Then I put a bit of the *Brun* under the eyes, close to the lashes, on the outer part."

"At night I do the same shaping, using darker colors and pastels like lilac and lapis blue, or pale amethyst and emerald green. I highlight with *Madeleine Mono's Iridescent Powder*."

"Both day and night, I curl my lashes, and apply 2 coats of mascara."

"I brush my eyebrows up. I use a bit of hairspray on a small brush and use that to brush my brows. They grow downwards."

"I use a rosy beige or coral blusher for day, and apply it where a natural blush would be, plus a bit above the brows. At night, I use *Calvin Klein's Cocoa Powder Contour* for contouring, and I brush on a deeper blush. I sometimes use *Chanel's Highlighter* on the top of my cheekbone and continue it upwards to blend in under the brows. It makes the hollows of the cheeks more noticeable in contrast."

"Sometimes I use a clear, slightly pink, lip gloss. Or a matte finish lipstick. *Lancome's China Rose* is a good color, with amethyst and blue on the eyes. I line my lips first, with a shade that matches the lipstick."

"I use *Laszlo's Controlling Face Powder.*"

## TERESA MA

*A former correspondent for the Far Eastern Economic Review, Teresa Ma is now an investment analyst with Jardine Fleming, the Hong Kong merchant bank. She was born in Hong Kong, spent her childhood in Thailand where her parents still reside, and received her B.A. from the University of Windsor, in Canada.*

### TERESA'S MAKEUP

"I am serious about my career. I started working as an economic journalist when I was nineteen, and I've felt that people wouldn't take me seriously if I wore too much makeup. People can be very conservative in their attitudes toward women and their appearance."

"I line my eyes with brown eyeliner, and I wear lipstick, a gloss, during the day."

"In the evening I add mascara, black, and use a coral blusher. I wear a bright red lipstick, not shiny, and use a blue-gray eyeshadow."

"I wash my face often during the day, and I carry moisturizer in my purse and use it after each washing. My skin is dry."

"I use a moisturizer morning and night, too, each time I wash my face. I use *Clinique*—their soap, tonic, and moisturizer."

"I think a good night's sleep is the best beauty treatment you can have. I'm allergic to scent, so I don't wear any. All of my makeup is *Clinique*."

"I shampoo my hair every day and use a conditioner."

## CAROLE KAI

*The vivacious Carole Kai is a former singer and entertainer who gave up starring roles in the entertainment field to return to Hawaii and devote herself to charity fund-raising activities. She is a music graduate of the University of Hawaii and was First Runner-up and Miss Popularity in the annual Cherry Blossom Festival held in Hawaii. A budding career in the entertainment field took her to Hollywood, then to Las Vegas, where she was nominated as the city's "Most Promising Newcomer." But she became a born-again Christian and decided to return to Hawaii to help the Variety Club School for children with learning disabilities, of which she is director of public affairs. Selected as one of twelve outstanding women of Hawaii, Carole is slowly returning to show business and divides her time between Los Angeles and Honolulu.*

### CAROLE'S MAKEUP

"I have dark, olive skin, and need dramatic colors to come alive."

"I use *Clinique Moisturizer*, and an eyeshadow base, *Ultima II*, that also moisturizes. I use this base to keep the shadow color from disappearing as the day progresses."

"My *Revlon Foundation*—it's called *Blushing Beige*—has a sunscreen. I use a little powder blush and contour my cheeks with it."

"For lining my eyes—the top and bottom—I use a teal liner pencil. Then I smudge the lining with black eyeshadow for a dusty softer look."

"From the top, I highlight the area below the brow with *Pink Petallo* by *Borghese*. Then just above the eye socket I use a cinnamon and black combination to contour my Asian eyes and give them a deep-set look. I fill in the area above the lashline with *Plum Florin* and *Black*, a mixture, by *Borghese*. I always darken the outer edges of my eyes for a more dramatic effect."

"I use a raspberry lipliner and fill in the lips with a moist lipstick by *Revlon*, usually in a cranberry color."

"I always try to drink 8 to 10 glasses of water a day. It really helps to cleanse the body of impurities."

"In the morning I do 15 minutes of stretching, then drink three glasses of water, and then start washing my face. I use *Neutrogena Soap*."

"At night, I always pat eye cream around my eyes. Then I massage my face with natural collagen cream."

"I have no product loyalty. I check the ingredients before buying creams and night creams. I never buy anything with mineral oil in it."

## ACKNOWLEDGMENTS

Many thanks to Suga, for his clear, positive information about hairstyling for Asians, and Fumio Kawashima of Peek-a-Boo who contributed valuable hairstyling and care information.

Thanks to Kimi Oshiro of Shiseido who took us into her styling studio, Arthur Scott of New York who talked about techniques, and Tyen of Christian Dior, Paris, who shared his knowledge of Asian faces and creative makeup.

Many thanks to Dr. Kiyoshi Toda of Tokyo Teishin Hospital, and Dr. Carole Shear of the Mother Cabrini Medical Center, for their time and information.

I especially thank the women who generously shared their beauty regimens.

And thanks to Fumiko Hamada, who tested every technique, including the many we discarded, and to Lisa Oyama, my editor.

定価3,000円
in Japan